TECHNOLOGY
IN EARLY
AMERICA

Needs and Opportunities for Study

The Institute of Early American History and Culture
is sponsored jointly by the College of William and
Mary and Colonial Williamsburg, Incorporated.

NEEDS AND OPPORTUNITIES
FOR STUDY SERIES

WHITFIELD J. BELL, JR.
Early American Science

WILLIAM N. FENTON
American Indian and White Relations to 1830
with a bibliography by L. H. Butterfield,
Wilcomb E. Washburn, and William N. Fenton

BERNARD BAILYN
Education in the Forming of American Society

WALTER MUIR WHITEHILL
The Arts in Early American History
with a bibliography by Wendell D. Garrett
and Jane N. Garrett

BROOKE HINDLE
Technology in Early American History
with a directory by
Lucius F. Ellsworth

PUBLISHED FOR THE

Institute of Early American History and Culture

AT WILLIAMSBURG, VIRGINIA

BY

The University of North Carolina Press

CHAPEL HILL

TECHNOLOGY IN EARLY AMERICA

NEEDS AND OPPORTUNITIES FOR STUDY

BY BROOKE HINDLE

WITH A DIRECTORY

OF ARTIFACT COLLECTIONS

BY LUCIUS F. ELLSWORTH

THE INSTITUTE
CONFERENCES

This is the fifth publication in the Needs and Opportunities for Study series of the Institute of Early American History and Culture. Each volume has been the outgrowth of a conference to explore a special historical field which scholars have neglected or indifferently exploited or in which renewed interest has developed in our own times. In each case a scholar has been invited to survey and appraise the subject. Whether it be early American arts and crafts, education or religion, science or technology, we seek to stimulate fresh research on specific topics by providing a wide-ranging view that correlates what has been done with what needs to be done.

These conferences began on a small scale in 1952, with local funds and with participants almost exclusively from the local area. A grant from the Fund for the Advancement of Education, through its Committee on the Role of Education in American History, made possible a larger and more diversified attendance at the conference on early American education in October 1959. Likewise the session on the arts in March 1964 became a cooperative undertaking of the Institute with Colonial Williamsburg, Inc., the Archives of American Art, and the Henry Francis du Pont Winterthur Museum.

The conference on early American technology, held on October 15, 1965, was the first of the series to meet outside Williamsburg. Since it was sponsored jointly by the Institute and the Eleutherian Mills-Hagley Foundation, Incorporated, it seemed most appropriate that the participants should convene in the Eleutherian Mills Historical Library and the Hagley Museum, amid their significant collections on early American industry. The interpretive essay by Brooke Hindle on "The Exhilaration of Early American Technology," circulated in advance of the meeting, was summarized by Whitfield J. Bell, Jr., of the American Philosophical Society in Mr. Hindle's absence. Then followed provocative commentary by Eugene S. Ferguson of Iowa State University and Daniel J. Boorstin

of the University of Chicago. Mr. Hindle's comprehensive bibliographical essay in tentative form had also been distributed in advance
so that it served likewise as basis for comment. During the afternoon
session Lucius F. Ellsworth emphasized artifacts as historical sources for
the study of technology and subsequently prepared the directory of
artifact collections included in the present volume. Melvin Kranzberg
of the Case Institute of Technology presided over the general discussion. The recording of the conference was transcribed and in light of
the proceedings Mr. Hindle revised his essays for publication. They
provide perspective and specifics for new research and interpretation that
may well begin with this book.

FOREWORD

In a dual sense Brooke Hindle's survey of needs and opportunities in early American technology is an appropriate sequel to Whitfield J. Bell, Jr.'s survey a decade ago of *Early American Science.* In terms of historical sequence pure science has usually illuminated the way for applied science, the natural sciences providing the basis for the useful arts, even though it be acknowledged that the latter often stimulate new discoveries in the former. In terms of historical research the history of science has antedated the history of technology; indeed, the evolution of science in certain contexts may be entirely unrelated to the useful arts, but it is well nigh inconceivable that a meaningful study of technology could be detached from the history of science, even during the American colonial period, for example, when the role of science in this respect was very limited. Although American technology has been overwhelmingly pragmatic in character and, as John B. Rae has remarked, Americans are inclined to equate "know-how" with technical skill,[1] scientific principles nevertheless have an undeniable role to play.

In his essay written in 1953 Mr. Bell pointed out that the history of science as an academic discipline was relatively new. The influence of George Sarton among American as well as European scholars after World War I and the transplanting of *Isis* from Europe to the United States aroused the interest of scientists in the history of their own disciplines. By the mid-1950's Bell noted that the work of these "devoted scholars is now being augmented by that of general historians, who bring to the history of science the understanding of social background and causation."[2] In fact, Brooke Hindle's study of *The Pursuit of Science in Revolutionary America, 1735–1789* (1956) is a perfect illustration of this point. His treatment of the subject became a contribution to intellectual

1. John B. Rae, " 'The Know-How' Tradition: Technology in American History," *Technology and Culture*, 1 (1959–60), 141.
2. Whitfield J. Bell, Jr., *Early American Science: Needs and Opportunities for Study* (Williamsburg, Va., 1955), 3.

and cultural history, enlightening to the humanist as well as the scientist. History of science by the scientist without historical perspective no longer meets with approval among well informed colleagues; at the same time the historian attracted to this field may encounter problems he is ill equipped to solve without assistance from the scientist. Since the publication of Bell's survey, mutual interest and collaboration have accelerated the advancement of knowledge in the history of early American science to such a degree that Mr. Bell is preparing a revised edition of his book.

Although Mr. Hindle's bibliographical essay in the present work discloses a wide chronological range of speculation and practice concerned with processes and machines in early American history, these fruits of scholarship which envision the development of technology as an integral part of cultural history have appeared only in recent years. It is this very situation that makes Mr. Hindle's work especially pertinent and timely. Two notable achievements supply the essential backdrops for the present stage on which the accelerating tempo of scholarly activity calls for intelligent direction. The five-volume collaborative work, *A History of Technology* (Oxford, 1955–58), edited by Charles Singer and associates, was designed "to provide students of technology and applied science with some humane and historical background for their studies," and thus with "a longer perspective of the ways in which the immensely complex technical knowledge of our civilization has come into being." [3] Viewing the plan of the work in retrospect, Dr. Singer reiterated the concept that "a history of technology should be clearly related to human history as a whole." [4] Although he and his collaborators were criticized for concentrating too much on "a history of how things have been done or made," [5] their perspective was commendable and their essays marked the beginnings for much future research.

The second achievement, and a continuing influence, was the founding of the Society for the History of Technology in 1958 and the launching of its quarterly journal, *Technology and Culture*, the following year. Two points are worth noting in this connection. The parent organization, the American Society for Engineering Educaton, had already called attention to the great interest among all academic disciplines in the development of technology; and the magazine announced in its first issue that the new Society and its publication must be interdisci-

3. Charles Singer and others, eds., *A History of Technology*, I, v.
4. Singer, "How *A History of Technology* Came into Being," *Technology and Culture*, 1 (1959–60), 306.
5. Singer and others, *History*, I, v; Robert S. Woodbury, "The Scholarly Future of the History of Technology," *Technology and Culture*, 1 (1959–60), 346.

plinary in scope. Echoing Dr. Singer's objectives, Editor Melvin Kranzberg of *Technology and Culture* declared, "We are concerned not only
with the history of technological devices and processes, but also with
the relations of technology to science, politics, social change, economics,
and the arts and humanities." [6] The title of the magazine is significant.
Its pages, like those of the monumental *History*, have provided a highly
desirable association of American technology with comparable historical
problems in other countries and other ages. Its editorial policy gives further assurance of significant contributions to scholarship from research
in depth as well as from interpretation on a broad scale.

A third factor in this recent expansion in the history of technology
is the revitalized role of the museum as a creative educational institution, collecting and preserving three-dimensional sources according to
plan, supplemented by manuscript, printed, and graphic records. To
amuse is no longer its primary aim; rather it is to engage in research and
publication and in so doing to make its exhibits more meaningful to
the scholar as well as to the general public. As the museum ceases to
be a storage house for curios, its "hardware" takes on new documentary
significance and its curator greater responsibilities toward scholarship.
For the history of technology three-dimensional "manufacts" (to adopt
an archaic expression recoined by Wilcomb E. Washburn) are indispensable.[7] Hence the pertinence of Lucius F. Ellsworth's directory of
artifact collections in the present volume.

And now Brooke Hindle's essays, the one interpretive and interroga-
tive, the other bibliographical and comprehensive in scope, traverse the
whole field with keen insight. It is a timely survey, cutting a bench-mark
for future measurements and assessments, a new starting point for scholarly research, a stimulus to historical synthesis. For the first time the
study of American technology will benefit from historical perspective
on ingenious ideas and mechanical processes correlated with the "things"
that have survived or can be reconstructed. Scholars will become fully
aware of the rich variety of sources for historical study and the adaptations of historical method required for intelligent exploitation of the
"physical remains," whether apart from or in conjunction with the written record. After surveying several well-worn approaches to the history
of technology and the merits and shortcomings of each, Mr. Hindle
analyzes the problems of preservation and the use of three-dimensional
"records"—visual examination which yields not only immediate data

6. Melvin Kranzberg, "At the Start [of the Magazine]," *Technology and Culture*,
1 (1959–60), 1.
7. "Manuscripts and Manufacts," *The American Archivist*, 27 (1964),, 245–50.

but clues to further research; reconstruction of machines and their operations under known historical conditions; the relation of handicraft to machine technology, the study of which has been retarded by the traditional gulf between the art museum and the industrial museum. Akin to this transition are problems of chronology in early American technology about which oversimplification and inadequate data have led to erroneous conclusions. In attempting to delimit this special field for the conference on needs and opportunities for study, it seemed clear that early American history extended far beyond 1815 (the customary date set by the Institute). Mr. Hindle's survey makes a strong case for the year 1850.

Finally, having considered certain key problems in the historian's approach to and use of the myriad sources peculiar to the study of technology, or shared with scholars in other disciplines, Mr. Hindle asks some provocative questions that will undoubtedly affect the "new" history of early American technology—questions concerning invention, processes, "hardware," and, not least, the men who were an integral part of this notable development, men who experienced the "exhilaration" that he emphasizes in the title of his essay. He wants the historian "to stand at the center of the technology—on the inside looking out," the better to assure that technology will have "its proper place within the context of early American history."

In 1959 Robert S. Woodbury, considering the scholarly future of the history of technology, observed that "its study is in much the same state as was the history of science in the 1930's—and we have no Sarton!" [8] This amounted, in part, to a reiteration of Arthur M. Schlesinger's assertion twenty years ago that History should bridge the gap between the natural sciences and human nature, between technology and social and intellectual history.[9] Today Mr. Hindle sees "signs of more fruitful approaches to an understanding of the subject." His essays constitute the most significant contribution to that end.

In addition to Mr. Hindle of New York University, scholars participating in the conference included John J. Beer, University of Delaware; Whitfield J. Bell, Jr., and Richard H. Shryock, American Philosophical Society; Daniel J. Boorstin, University of Chicago; David J. Brandenburg, American University; M. V. Brewington, Peabody Museum of

8. Woodbury, in *Technology and Culture*, 1 (1959–60), 345.
9. Arthur M. Schlesinger, "An American Historian Looks at Science and Technology," *Isis*, 36 (1946), 166.

Salem; Carl Condit, Northwestern University; A. Hunter Dupree, University of California at Berkeley; Eugene S. Ferguson, Iowa State University; Marshall W. Fishwick, Wemyss Foundation; Constance M. Green, Washington, D.C.; E. N. Hartley, Thomas P. Hughes, Cyril E. Smith, and Robert S. Woodbury, Massachusetts Institute of Technology; Charles F. Hummel, Winterthur Museum; Melvin Kranzberg and Robert E. Schofield, Case Institute of Technology; W. David Lewis, State University of New York at Buffalo; Hugo Meier, Pennsylvania State University; Robert P. Multhauf, Smithsonian Institution; Carroll W. Pursell, Jr., University of California at Santa Barbara; Nathan Reingold, Library of Congress; Minor Wine Thomas, New York State Historical Association; Sam B. Warner, Jr., Washington University; and Peter C. Welsh, Smithsonian Institution. The Eleutherian Mills-Hagley Foundation was represented by Lucius F. Ellsworth, George H. Gibson, David T. Gilchrist, Walter J. Heacock, Philip J. Kimball, George Rogers Taylor, Norman B. Wilkinson, and Richmond D. Williams. William W. Abbot, Lester J. Cappon, and James Morton Smith represented the Institute of Early American History and Culture. The members of the Advisory Committee of the Eleutherian Mills-Hagley Foundation also attended both discussion sessions.

By correspondence and conversation Walter J. Heacock, then director of the Hagley Museum and now general director of the Eleutherian Mills-Hagley Foundation, and I developed the basic plan for the conference along lines of its predecessors in the Institute's series. Later on David T. Gilchrist, W. David Lewis, Norman B. Wilkinson, and Richmond D. Williams of the Library and Museum, and William W. Abbot and James Morton Smith of the Institute staff gave valuable assistance in working out the detailed plans. Since the sessions were held at the Library and Museum, the burden of local arrangements fell entirely upon Mr. Heacock and his colleagues, to whom I express hearty appreciation on behalf of the Institute. Likewise we in Williamsburg (and I am sure I can speak for all the participants in the conference) are grateful to the Eleutherian Mills-Hagley Foundation, Incorporated, which provided the financial support for the sessions and the generous hospitality that enhanced them. The Institute assumed responsibility for editing and publication of the conference proceedings.

A special acknowledgment with thanks is due Melvin Kranzberg for his lively services as chairman; to Whitfield J. Bell, Jr., for an able summary of Brooke Hindle's essay and bibliography; to Daniel J. Boorstin and Eugene S. Ferguson for their provocative comments; and to Lucius F. Ellsworth for his illuminating remarks supplementing his Directory of Artifact Collections. The heart of the conference, of course, was Brooke Hindle's stimulating essays which, read in advance by the participants, had already aroused their enthusiasm for discussion. To Mr. Hindle rightly goes the warmest words of appreciation and gratitude.

Williamsburg, 22 June 1966   Lester J. Cappon, *Director*

ACKNOWLEDGMENTS

In preparing my essays for the Conference and in revising them for this book, I received the most understanding cooperation from the staffs of the Institute of Early American History and Culture and the Eleutherian Mills-Hagley Foundation. The proceedings of the Conference and the suggestions made separately by the participants extended and deepened my understanding; especially important was the help of Whitfield J. Bell, Jr., and Eugene S. Ferguson. Additional aid came from Charles E. Peterson of Philadelphia and Rex Wailes of Beaconsfield, England. Again, my wife was my most constant reliance. Portions of these essays rest upon work pursued under a Guggenheim Fellowship held in 1964–65, and under grants received from the Arts and Sciences Research Fund of New York University.

Lucius F. Ellsworth wishes to acknowledge the help of his wife, Jeanne M. Ellsworth; his colleagues at the Eleutherian Mills-Hagley Foundation, Norman B. Wilkinson, Walter J. Heacock, and George H. Gibson; Minor Wine Thomas of the New York State Historical Association at Cooperstown; W. David Lewis, State University of New York at Buffalo; and Peter C. Welsh at the Smithsonian Institution. He also wishes to thank collectively the personnel at the museums he visited.

B. H.

CONTENTS

TECHNOLOGY
IN EARLY
AMERICA

Needs and Opportunities for Study

THE EXHILARATION
OF EARLY AMERICAN
TECHNOLOGY: AN ESSAY

by Brooke Hindle

The central role of technology in early American history has only recently begun to receive some of the attention it requires. Strikingly, the craftsmen, mechanics, engineers, and entrepreneurs who built that technology were enthusiastically—even ebulliently—aware of the pervasive significance of their work. Historians have not been unresponsive, but they have often been uninformed and they have usually been too preoccupied with other investigations to give it serious study. Thus, the history of technology, invigorating and stimulating as it is, has not yet reached an academic status parallel to other fields of history. But increasingly specialists who have cultivated corners of the field and general historians who have admitted an oblique interest are being joined in Europe and in America by historians competent in the field of technology.

The European interest in the history of technology opened first and probably most effectively—certainly most relevantly to the American story—in England. There it was moved forward by a train of enthusiasts, such as Samuel Smiles, and by the continuing effectiveness of such institutions as the Science Museum and the Newcomen Society. The new *Journal of Industrial Archaeology*, along with the surrounding publication and preservation projects in Great Britain, are promising steps in the direction of informed specialization. Many of the recent British books on the history of technology, notably Singer's five-volume *History of Technology*, offer increasingly significant contributions by academic historians.[1] Continental interest has also risen, but it remains closely

1. Charles Singer *et al.*, eds., *History of Technology*, 5 vols. (London, 1954–58).

associated with technological museums—as evidenced in Daumas' continuing *Histoire* and in Klemm's lecture survey.[2] In the Iron Curtain countries, political dogma has encouraged an interest in the history of technology, an emphasis reflected in publications and in the 1965 International Congress of the History of Science, which met in Poland.

In the United States, the growth of a new interest and a new approach has several roots and supports. Most apparent are the formation of the Society for the History of Technology in 1958, the issuance of its journal, *Technology and Culture*, and the development of a program in the history of technology at Case Institute of Technology—all under the stimulus of Melvin Kranzberg. Similarly, at other educational institutions academic work is arising; probably the largest concentration of scholars interested in the history of technology is to be found at the Massachusetts Institute of Technology. At the same time the newly invigorated Museum of History and Technology of the Smithsonian Institution has become a center for much important activity in the field, and smaller museums are beginning to acquire academically oriented personnel. The Eleutherian Mills-Hagley Foundation is the best example of new institutions with a scholarly approach to the history of technology.

Of the numerous approaches that have been opened to the history of technology, that of the history of science seems the most directly pertinent. The History of Science Society and its organs have always professed to include technology within their scope; under its present editor, Robert P. Multhauf, *Isis* is markedly interested in the subject. George Sarton, who did so much to define the field, included technology within his great work, and it remains a component of the annual "Critical Bibliography" which he founded. Formally, then, the history of technology has a home within the history of science, yet it has long been clear that technology does not occupy a central place in the efforts of this group and that some members regard it as a distinctly alien element.

Basically, the tensions surrounding the relationship between science and technology point to fundamental differences between the two and, even more pointedly, to differences in the historical course which each followed. Science and technology have different objectives. Science seeks basic understanding—ideas and concepts usually expressed in linguistic or mathematical terms. Technology seeks means for making and doing things. It is a question of process, always expressible in terms of three-

2. Maurice Daumas, *Histoire Générale des Techniques* (Paris, 1962—); Friedrich Klemm, *A History of Western Technology*, trans. Dorothy Waley Singer (New York, 1959).

dimensional "things." In the early American period, tools and means, as well as products, were all usually three-dimensional; but even when the product was not, as in the electric telegraph, the means were.

The relationship between science and technology has varied in time and place. During the Middle Ages the great technological advances owed little to science or to those who pursued science. On the other hand, those engaged in the space technology of the present are sometimes at a loss to draw a line between the science and the technology they use. Schofield and Gillispie have helped to illuminate the far from obvious relationships between the two in eighteenth-century Europe.[3]

In colonial America the role of science in technology was certainly very limited, but the Americans entered on independence amid many Baconian intentions of applying science. Mechanics who called for "principles" had in mind the tabular test results of modern engineering handbooks rather than science. In the nineteenth century, however, the literature reveals well-conceived efforts to use science. The results have not been seriously studied, but appearances suggest that the prevailing British generalization was correct: American technology depended but little upon the "sober reasoning of science."[4]

Richard H. Shryock has suggested that the Americans were most successful with those elements of "technology applied to specific and single objectives" and less concerned with "the more general or abstract technology." As examples, he cited the cotton gin, a machine of limited applicability, and the dental techniques in which the Americans pioneered. Technology regarded in this light might then be labeled either "applied" or "basic," following a familiar division of science. Accepting this distinction, Robert S. Woodbury pointed out that the idea of a highly specialized machine tool was distinctly American but, on the other hand, that some of the basic machine tools were also American—notably the milling machine. Carl W. Condit suggested that the concept of basic technology might be related to the emerging scientific character of technology and that the Americans were generally indifferent to this sort of theory.[5]

Yet science inescapably looms in the background of all technology and offers the historian one of his best tools for evaluating past technolo-

3. Robert E. Schofield, "The Industrial Orientation of Science in the Lunar Society of Birmingham," *Isis*, 48 (1957), 408–15; Charles C. Gillispie, "The Discovery of the Leblanc Process," *ibid.*, 152–67.

4. Oliver Evans, *Abortion of the Young Steam Engineer's Guide* (Philadelphia, 1805), 22; Thomas Tredgold, *The Steam Engine*, 2 vols. (London, 1838), I, 43.

5. All of these comments were made at the Conference on Early American Technology held at the Hagley Museum, October 15–16, 1965, cited hereafter as Early American Technology Conference.

gies. He must certainly be cognizant of the state of science in the period whose technology he studies.

Further, the historians of science have met problems in their study which must similarly be faced by those who study the history of technology. Specifically, the old dictum that one must be a competent scientist before he can approach the history of science has generally given way to an insistence that he possess both the historian's viewpoint and a good working knowledge of the science under study. The parallel answer for technology would ask not that the student be an engineer but rather that he be a historian with a good knowledge of the technology—and the related science—he studies.

Yet a different answer is implicit in another approach to the history of technology—that of the practicing engineer with a deep interest in the history of his profession. Some of the most useful work on early American technology has been done by just such men; for example, by Roe, Bathe, and Steinman.[6] Their insights depend, inextricably, upon their experiences, and our understanding will be poorer if it cannot continue to draw from this reservoir. At the same time, as other fields of history have advanced in professionalism—the history of medicine and military history, for example—they have depended less extensively upon the practitioners of the professions under study.

Of the older approaches to the history of technology, economic history has probably been the most productive. In the absence of any field of the history of technology until very recently, economic historians have supplied many of the available surveys and monographs. Thus, the surveys of manufacturing in the United States by Clark and by Bishop are presented in terms of economic history.[7] So is the fine access to early iron technology offered by Bining, to woolen manufacturing technology by Cole, and to textile and machine tool production by Gibb and by Navin.[8] Yet technology was never more than a part of their story—one of the factors of production.

6. Among their many works are: Joseph W. Roe, *English and American Tool Builders* (N.Y., 1916); Greville and Dorothy Bathe, *Oliver Evans: A Chronicle of Early American Engineering* (Phila., 1935); and David B. Steinman, *The Builders of the Bridge: the Story of John Roebling and his Son* (N.Y., 1945).

7. Victor S. Clark, *History of Manufactures in the United States, 1607–1870* (Washington, 1916); J. Leander Bishop, *A History of American Manufactures from 1608 to 1860*, 3 vols. (Phila., 1861–68).

8. Arthur C. Bining, *Pennsylvania Iron Manufacture in the Eighteenth Century* (Harrisburg, 1938); Arthur H. Cole, *The American Wool Manufacture*, 2 vols. (Cambridge, Mass., 1926); George S. Gibb, *The Saco-Lowell Shops: Textile Machinery Building in New England, 1813–1949* (Cambridge, Mass., 1950); Thomas R. Navin, *The Whitin Machine Works since 1831* (Cambridge, Mass., 1950).

From a similar background of economic history, a few recent writers do give primary attention to technology. This is conspicuously true of Hunter in his *Steamboats on the Western Rivers*, and we may anticipate that it will be even more so in his forthcoming book on power.[9] Of the studies which start from a consideration of economic growth, two place technology at the center of their inquiry: Strassman and Habakkuk.[10] Since it is almost never possible to separate technology entirely from the economic process, economic history and even economic theory offer rich insights which even those whose central concern is physical technology should seek.

One of the less obvious but often relevant approaches is that of the local historian. Even the most general local surveys tend to show concern for social history and for physical survivals, often preserving information that might otherwise have been lost as a result of the prevailing neglect by academic historians during the late nineteenth and early twentieth centuries. A good example of this sort of repository is Scharf and Westcott's history of Philadelphia.[11] Regions, states, and towns have been delineated in this manner, while other local historians have focused their efforts topically. In a different category are more specialized local studies which can also be described as economic studies or, in the case of Green and Shlakman, almost as technological studies.[12] There have been many local studies of technology, from the early industrial surveys of Freedley to the recent small specialized studies of Harry B. Weiss.[13]

Literary and philosophical approaches to early American technology have been much neglected, although there is a considerable body of contemporary and late nineteenth-century writings to be studied and evaluated. The recent work by Leo Marx is the best examination of the literary impact of technology, a product of the American Studies approach.[14] Critiques of philosophical character tend to be recent in empha-

9. Louis C. Hunter, *Steamboats on the Western Rivers* (Cambridge, Mass., 1949).

10. W. Paul Strassman, *Risk and Technological Innovation: American Manufacturing Methods during the Nineteenth Century* (Ithaca, 1959); H. J. Habakkuk, *American and British Technology in the Nineteenth Century* (Cambridge, Eng., 1962).

11. John Thomas Scharf and Thompson Westcott, *History of Philadelphia, 1609–1884*, 3 vols. (Phila., 1884).

12. Constance McLaughlin Green, *History of Naugatuck, Connecticut* (New Haven, 1949); Vera Shlakman, *Economic History of a Factory Town: A Study of Chicopee, Massachusetts* (Northampton, 1935).

13. For example, Edwin T. Freedley, *Philadelphia and Its Manufactures* (Phila., 1859); Harry B. and Grace M. Weiss, *Forgotten Mills of Early New Jersey* (Trenton, 1960).

14. Leo Marx, *The Machine in the Garden* (N.Y., 1964).

sis, as is Boorstin's, and aesthetic in direction, as is Kouwenhoven's.[15]

Very different is the anthropological approach to technology. Regarding history in terms of identifiable cultures, it is responsive to technological elements and often emphasizes them. This is distinctly true of Anthony N. B. Garvan's Index of American Cultures, being developed at the University of Pennsylvania, which is based upon selected culture regions studied intensively within brief time spans. Here, known artifacts, literary as well as three-dimensional, are photographed and described on cards. They are then keyed into an elaborate index. This may offer both specific details and suggestions on method to the historian of technology.[16]

Somewhat related is the archaeological manner of studying the past, most familiar in terms of digging for the remains of ancient civilizations. On a local level, and with relevance to more recent society, archaeology has always been better supported in England than in the United States. The English activity in industrial archaeology builds upon a rich heritage. Several restorations have supported archaeological efforts in this country; their technological relevance is great in all cases but highest when industrial plants rather than manor houses are investigated. Good work of this sort is currently being done under the direction of Ivor Noël Hume at Colonial Williamsburg and by the National Park Service at several sites. Much more investigation, directed specifically to technological objectives, is in order.

The aesthetic evaluation of technology and its products dominates several categories of writings which are useful to the historian of technology. Especially valuable are the many highly competent studies of architecture and of the history of architecture. Because architecture combines art and engineering in a peculiarly intimate fashion, good architectural historians are always conscious of the technological elements in their story and they usually write about them. Primary attention to the technology of architecture—that is, the study of building —is more rare. Marcus Whiffen's books include building technology within architectural history.[17] Condit's fine work is a pioneering isolation of the technology involved.[18]

15. Daniel J. Boorstin, *The Image, or What Happened to the American Dream* (N.Y., 1962); John A. Kouwenhoven, *Made in America: the Arts in Modern Civilization* (Garden City, 1948).

16. Garvan explains his project in "Historical Depth in Comparative Culture Study," *American Quarterly*, 14 (1962), 260–74.

17. For example, Marcus Whiffen, *The Eighteenth-Century Houses of Williamsburg: A Study of Architecture and Building in the Colonial Capital of Virginia* (Williamsburg, 1960).

18. Carl W. Condit, *American Building Art: The Nineteenth Century* (N.Y., 1960).

The aesthetic approach is strong also in another, more diffuse, group of writings, the work of antiquarians and collectors of art objects. These range from erudite, highly disciplined evaluations by connoisseurs and museum personnel to loosely arranged catalogs by enthusiasts with little knowledge of history or of the technology represented in the products they collect. In total, these works contain mountains of data about one craft after another. Among them can be found specific details, fine photographs, and an understanding of both products and manufacturing techniques. The best treatment has been given to items that have retained a high monetary value with collectors; for example: silverware, glassware, pottery, furniture, and coins. Gun collectors, proceeding from similar motivation, have compiled material of more obvious technological value because of the nature of the product. The whole of this work ought not to be scorned because some is of poor quality and because technology is secondary in all of it. Much can be read back from the product into the manner of making it.

Leading art museums have played a central role in stimulating the study of craft products and their manufacture—the Henry Francis du Pont Winterthur Museum and the Boston Museum of Fine Arts are especially active in this work. Useful museum publications are voluminous but, because of their frequently scattered and occasional character, hard to find and use. The best libraries often do not hold this sort of pamphlet material or do not catalog it in a manner calculated to aid the historian of technology. Yet particularly where museums have turned to laboratory analysis of their holdings, acquaintance with their activities is essential. Indeed, Cyril S. Smith has urged the necessity of acquiring the insights of the art historian.[19]

A special plea should be entered for those collectors who are motivated neither by the aesthetic nor by the monetary value of the product. Such are the members of the Early American Industries Association who collect examples of and data upon the tools and products of primarily pre-machine technologies. Otherwise known as the "Pick and Shovel Club," this group has met from convention to convention at Dearborn, Shelburne, Mystic, and the Hagley Museum. It prints in its *Chronicle* a great variety of scattered information, and some of its members have published useful books. The various folk museums and local museums preserve similar "homely" artifacts which reflect very directly the way life was lived—how things were made and done. Specific details about technology are more elusive and more easily lost than may be imagined. All such information needs to be cherished.

The efforts of these varied collectors highlight a central problem

19. **Early American Technology Conference.**

in all history of technology: what can be done and what ought to be done with the artifacts and physical remains from the technologies under study? The physical things of technology in many ways remain the ultimate source for the history of technology. Preserved products and tools as well as other traces left by these technologies—including railroad cuts and canal segments, razed factories and mine shafts—constitute repositories of information poorly understood by the general historian. Furthermore, there are many barriers in the way of their optimum use. A start can be made by recognizing the primary problems, but it is not likely that many can be solved except by a rather considerable joint endeavor.

To begin with, there is no simple difference or conflict between words and things—words do not represent ideas alone nor things mere material accomplishment.[20] With technology as with all other aspects of man's life, words serve the function of describing and translating into a transmissible medium. When combined with engineering drawings, mathematical and chemical formulae, photographs, and sound recordings, they can render the artifacts and machines of technology in forms that can be stored compactly and multiplied without limit. Words can do more; they can be used to evaluate and compare physical objects and their functions. They can even follow the projections of technology into the abstractions of poetry and aspiration.

Nevertheless, the "things" of technology retain a primacy that does not adhere to the physical objects associated with science, religion, politics, or any intellectual or social pursuit. The means of technology are physical; the objectives of technology are also physical or material. Three-dimensional physical objects are the expression of technology—in the same way that paintings and sculpture are the expression of the visual arts. They call for some of the same attention and celebration that is accorded to works of art.

Moreover, although it is technically possible to reduce a steam engine to a variety of paper-and-tape records, this has not been done. At best, the scholar has available to him only rough descriptions, specifications, sketches, and photographs. These may very well suffice for his ordinary needs but they do not provide all of the transmissible information that can be gathered. Conversely, it often happens that absolutely nothing is available save the specimen itself, preserved in an out-of-the-way museum which lacks even a full-time staff. The scholar must then get what he can from a visual inspection, with inadequate light and space.

20. Cf. John A. Kouwenhoven, "American Studies: Words or Things?" in Marshall W. Fishwick, ed., *American Studies in Transition* (Phila., 1964), 15–35.

What can be gained from the visual examination of a technological specimen depends directly upon the knowledge and perceptiveness of the examiner. If he is well acquainted with similar objects, he can compare and evaluate as he looks. The surface inspection of a plow, a gun, or a loom may yield insights which did not appear at all when the student examined a very good description or photograph. Fundamental characteristics as well as the aesthetic character and the quality of workmanship often appear very different after a visual inspection. The historian is not likely ever to agree that the best paper-and-tape rendition of a specimen is a satisfactory substitute—and today most specimens do not boast even a poor description.

However, there is much information inherent in any specimen that will not yield to a casual, visual inspection. The nature of this information varies with each category of artifact. For a simple metal casting, a spectrographic or chemical analysis may be useful. Such a chemical analysis was run on many of the iron stove plates in the Mercer Museum collection, permitting the examiner to assign their production to specific furnaces; this fundamental information could only be acquired by taking a plug from each specimen, but the operation had to be done only once.[21] Charles F. Hummel, and Theodore Z. Penn, a graduate student who worked in the Andelot-Copeland Museum Science Project of the Winterthur Museum and the University of Delaware, have described the application of optical spectroscopy to the dating and validation of brass artifacts through the identification of trace elements.[22]

With machines, data on working characteristics are the obvious need. Operating steam engines should be run at different speeds with different loads, indicator diagrams taken, and the results analyzed. Another useful approach is suggested in the sound motion pictures of old English engines taken by the Shell Film Unit under the stimulus of the Cornish Engines Preservation Society.[23] Most of the sounds of history are lost beyond recall, but those of some machinery can be recovered. The smells and other attributes of the past, especially of the perishable products of chemical technology, are still more elusive, although John J. Beer pointed out that they might be re-created to give added depth to restorations.[24]

Study and analysis could create a new species of source material whose value might become great if uniform tests and analyses were

21. B. F. Fackenthal, Jr., "Classification and Analysis of Stove Plates," Bucks County Historical Society, *Proceedings*, 4 (1917), 55–61.
22. Early American Technology Conference.
23. H. W. Dickinson, *The Cornish Engine: A Chapter in the History of Steam Power* (London, 1950).
24. Early American Technology Conference.

agreed upon for each category and applied to most of the remaining specimens. If at the same time uniform patterns for describing and picturing these specimens could be applied, historians would have at their command comparable, two-dimensional renditions of the three-dimensional objects of early American technology.

The big problem is the magnitude of the task; nothing similar has yet been done for the collections of a single museum.[25] Clearly, the maximum effort in recording the characteristics of a specimen is not likely to be feasible except where destruction of the original is anticipated or duplication in a three-dimensional model is planned. When the Deutsches Museum made a copy of the Science Museum's Watt and Boulton "Lap" steam engine, seventy sheets of engineering drawing were required. Similarly, where it is impossible to preserve all of the factories and plants noted in the British Industrial Monuments Survey, a large program has been projected to record the outstanding characteristics of those that will be destroyed; in some cases this work is already in progress.[26] The Historic American Buildings Survey, although not conceived primarily to preserve technological edifices, accumulated large files of drawings and photographs of many sorts of buildings of importance to historians of technology.

The historian does not require at his fingertips the maximum recordable information about each specimen; indeed, under most circumstances, this would be a burdensome supply of riches. By extended practice, numismatists and gun collectors have arrived at abbreviated descriptions and similar photographs and drawings which satisfy *their* needs in comparing, cataloging, and evaluating these technological products. Historians of technology could probably agree upon the minimum data *they* would need in studying each category of specimen. In arriving at standards, they should not disdain the example of the drawings offered in the ancient publications of Stuart, Strickland, Rees, and Nicholson.[27]

Even if such a program could be agreed upon, its fulfillment would

25. One of the best series of published technological catalogs is that of the Conservatoire National des Arts et Métiers in Paris.

26. This survey, under the guidance of Rex Wailes of the Ministry of Public Buildings and Works, is an aspect of a large movement coordinated in part by the Council for British Archaeology. Individuals and schools of architecture are cooperating in making drawings of designated buildings. New industrial museums are arising in different parts of the country and old ones are finding new life. The publication of a series of regional surveys has begun with Kenneth Hudson, *Industrial Archaeology of Southern England* (Devon, 1965).

27. Charles B. Stuart, *The Naval and Mail Steamers of the United States* (N. Y., 1853); William Strickland, E. H. Gill, and H. R. Campbell, eds., *Public Works of the United States of America* (London, 1841); John Nicholson, *The Operative Mechanic, and British Machinist* (1st Amer. edn., Phila., 1826); Abraham Rees, *Cyclopedia*, 39 vols. and 6 vols. plates (Phila., 1810–24).

require major financial support and continuing cooperation from individuals and institutions.[28] The need for it is manifestly greatest in describing and recording the collections of individuals and of marginal museums—the most difficult collections to handle. The major technological museums are not only friendly to scholarship but almost eager to serve it. They can be counted upon to support any efforts that clearly represent the desires of the scholarly community. Whether or not means are developed for handling three-dimensional technological specimens with some of the ease with which manuscripts can now be handled, scholars must place more of their reliance upon the collections available to them in museums. Important assistance is now offered them in the accompanying Directory of Artifact Collections prepared by Lucius F. Ellsworth.

In approaching artifact collections, the academic scholar should appreciate some of the difficulties faced by museums holding technological specimens—and, in some cases, related manuscripts and publications as well. Like all museums, they must serve two functions. First, they display their specimens in attractive settings, interpreting them to viewers in broad historical perspective—often with learning and originality. In this function they serve by far the larger number of their visitors, and to this function their support is often primarily directed. Second, they make available to scholars the specimens they hold and the research information their staffs have compiled about them.[29]

These two functions are not wholly separate but they cannot be combined as readily as is sometimes imagined. Consider, for example, the presentation of dioramas, small working models, or full-scale restorations incorporating parts of the original. Even in a restoration, only a small part of which is conjectural—and more obviously in all reconstructions—a portion of the result is guesswork. It may be well-researched, imaginative guesswork of the sort which every historian values, but it must be called guesswork, nevertheless.

The imaginative insights familiar to the historian are something else

28. Nathan Reingold regarded this objective as attainable although in a shape not yet discernible, but Robert S. Woodbury doubted whether people competent to carry it through were available. Early American Technology Conference.

29. There is remarkably little literature on the research function of a museum in relation to its display function. Three schools of thought are set forth by Wilcomb E. Washburn, "Scholarship and the Museum," Clark C. Evernham, "Science Education: A Museum Responsibility," and Katherine Coffey, "Operation of the Individual Museum," *Museum News*, 40 (1961), 16–29. For a brief appraisal in the field of architectural preservation, see Alan Gowans, "Preservation," *Journal of the Society of Architectural Historians*, 24 (1965), 252–53. Also see Ralph R. Miller, "Museum Installations," *The Museologist*, No. 95 (1965), 6–8, and Kenneth Hudson, "The Taming of Industrial Archaeology," *Museums Journal*, 65 (1965), 35–39.

again. In written history, the author may admit his lack of knowledge where it is inadequate, or he may omit all mention of episodes upon which information is defective. The builder of a model or a restoration does not have that option. If he has an original water wheel, he cannot erect it without supports because those are lacking; he must study similar wheels and supply his best guess about the missing elements. Nor can he paint the guesswork orange to indicate its conjectural character; that would destroy the illusion. Besides, he may have a drawing of the supporting structure, and his only uncertainty may concern the kind of wood used. Then the very limited nature of his guesswork would be harder still to indicate.

It remains very difficult for a scholar to know how much of a restoration is based upon original parts or reliable information. He may be able to discover how the figureheads differed in successive restorations of the *U.S.S. Constitution*, but how can he be sure that the present exterior finish is that of the fighting frigate? In the magnificent restoration at Saugus he is informed that the location of the water wheels serving the forge is based on archaeological evidence. But, without access to manuscript records, he has no clue to the sources for the arrangement and interior appearance of fires, hammers, and furnishings. Even if he recalls the almost exact similarity of the *Encyclopédie* plates, he is left wondering how much of the interior might be painted orange and how deep should be the color of the dye. Must not every conceivable restoration be surrounded with some such questions and doubts? [30]

Is there not then a need to bring the scholar closer to the sources than the visible restoration? Behind several restorations and museums there are very fine unpublished historical and engineering reports— upon which exhibits and restorations or reconstructions are based. At their best, they show precisely what is known and what is not; they discuss sources and similar specimens; they explore the historical setting.

Understandably, even the most generous museums and restorations are somewhat reluctant to open wide their research reports. They have not been written for publication or to stand the scrutiny of historians. Much that they contain is tentative. Errors may have been detected in

30. The interpretive function of museums and restorations has not attracted the attention it deserves. Perhaps the best statement, though restricted to anthropology, is H. H. Frese, *Anthropology and the Public: The Role of Museums* (Leiden, 1960). Osbert Lancaster discusses criteria for preservation of historic architectural artifacts in "Some Thoughts on Preservation," which will appear in *Historic Preservation Today* (1966), published jointly by the National Trust for Historic Preservation and Colonial Williamsburg. The appendix to that book also contains "A Report on Principles and Guidelines for Historic Preservation in the United States."

them, but time may not have been available to correct them. The sponsoring institutions often encourage their authors to continue their researches in the line of the reports and to publish their results in finished form. But the published works often become broader and more significant—at the sacrifice of some of the specific information contained in the original reports. From such beginnings have come many valuable publications—especially by staff members of the Museum of History and Technology, of the Eleutherian Mills-Hagley Foundation, and of Colonial Williamsburg. However, all museum publications remain difficult to control bibliographically; one of the great needs is the compilation of simple finding lists.

The need for the scholar to get behind the exhibit and the restoration can already be satisfied at some of the leading institutions. The unpublished research reports of the Hagley Museum and those of Colonial Williamsburg, both upon buildings and upon crafts, are available to competent researchers. Yet helpful as they are, reports can be no substitute for the more basic sources—contemporary writings and artifacts. As Eugene S. Ferguson put it, "The historian should consider looking at artifacts to be so much a part of his trade that he will, over the years, develop a keen critical sense regarding the authenticity and significance of the artifacts and restorations that he sees. To be used effectively, the artifacts must mean something to the historian directly, not once removed through the mind and eyes of a curator." [31]

The scholarly handling of the artifacts of technology involves another question of the first magnitude: how should the historian approach those products of the crafts which have become the province of the art museum and the collector? The art museum and the technological museum have drawn lines between their areas of concern which have the tacit approval of many historians of technology but which ought now to be re-examined. Folk and craft products, which to the outsider seem to have limited aesthetic value, have been drawn into the realm of the art museum along with the products of men who are more obviously "artists" rather than artisans. The interest of the art museum in machine products and industrial design is more limited—especially in the early American period. The art museum and the art historian may give careful attention to craft products, but the direction of their interest is aesthetic and, to some extent, social. On the other hand, the technological museum and, often, the historian of technology tend to place their primary attention upon machine production, recognizing the hand-production phase of their studies but relegating it to a kind of prehistory

31. Early American Technology Conference.

or embryonic stage of development—to some extent relinquishing hand production to the art museum and the art historian. This division is well marked in the respective domains of the Eleutherian Mills-Hagley Foundation and the Winterthur Museum in Wilmington, Delaware. It is a division followed by the Museum of History and Technology in Washington, the Franklin Institute in Philadelphia, and the Science Museum in London. It is altogether desirable from the viewpoint of specialization and good direction.

For the historian who pursues craft technology into the art museum, this division has the additional advantage of opening the extensive and fundamental relationships between technology and aesthetics. It also offers insights into craft technology developed over a long period of time by men who pursued the truth about the objects of their work— in whatever category of study it might fall. On the other hand, the historian is hampered by the disregard of craft technology on the part of the technological museum and the historian of technology. The satisfactory understanding of early American technology demands that the whole technology of the period be studied by the historian of technology. This may seem to call for aggression or imperialism on the part of the historian of technology, but it is essential for the integrity of his subject. The whole continuum of early American history must be brought within the scope of his study and subjected to similar research and reflection.

This need becomes doubly apparent as soon as the chronology of early American technology is examined—even in the roughest terms. The terminal date of 1850 for this book is one of convenience. It is supported however by the convergence of many lines of technological development which seem to attain measures of fulfillment in the 1840's and by the industrial exhibitions of the early 1850's which marked American achievement in a spectacular fashion.

The one chronological divide that cuts across the early period of American history is the separation of hand production from the introduction of the new machine manufacture. It is inescapable. In Mumford's periodization, the technology with which the colonists built the first foundations was paleotechnic, while the new machine technology was neotechnic.[32] The division is the same with those who have used less esoteric terms, whether they write of the introduction of steam power, the introduction of the technology of the Industrial Revolution, or the use of machine or mass production.

This division is inescapable but it is not sharp, and the difficulty is

32. Lewis Mumford, *Technics and Civilization* (N. Y., 1934), 151–267.

to state precisely what separated the earlier technology from the later. The earliest gristmills and iron plantations represented powered, machine operation—while at the other end of the period, individual handcraft continued to be a part of much production, in the shop and on the farm. Steam power was used as early as 1750, but as late as 1850 water power still dominated much industrial production and was still advancing in technological efficiency. Yet certainly between those two dates the great technological divide was crossed, not only in America but in Britain and western Europe as well. This fact dominates the logical desire of some of our best current scholars to dissociate their efforts from the initial, pre-machine technology—sometimes with vehemence, sometimes with indifference.

The technological aspect of the Industrial Revolution has been subjected to much criticism. On the point of a great technological divide, Daumas has argued that there was no technological revolution at all. John U. Nef suggests that there was a revolution but that the significant elements of change should be placed in an earlier period, in the sixteenth and seventeenth centuries. This would not only move the technological divide to closer coincidence with the scientific revolution but would place it prior to and during the early phases of American settlement.[33]

If these questions remain in doubt, then surely the historian of early American technology must study the whole of his terrain, *even if* his only interest is in the later, machine technology. The depth and chronology of the European divide does not, in any case, determine the depth and chronology of the American. This requires specific study of specifically American experience. The more the history of technology is studied, the more its significance in all periods of history emerges. Hopefully, more and more scholars will regard colonial technology as a valid study, whether "paleotechnic" or "neotechnic." The way the colonists made and did things is a fundamental part of their history—heightened in interest by the speed with which they transferred European techniques and the variety of adaptations and innovations they introduced.

The tentative identification of colonial technology as a hand-production, craft technology highlights one of the staggering coincidences of American history. The birth of the Republic coincided almost precisely

33. Maurice Daumas, "Le Mythe de la Revolution Technique," *Ithaca: Proceedings of the Tenth International Congress of the History of Science* (Paris, 1964), I, 415–18; John U. Nef, *The Conquest of the Material World: Essays on the Coming of Industrialism* (Chicago, 1964).

with the first efforts to introduce the power and textile machines of the Industrial Revolution. Whatever terms we use to describe it, the language and character of American technology altered abruptly between 1776 and 1850; at points it even advanced to world leadership. The organ tones with which the American mechanic in the 1830's and 1840's proclaimed his success in building better locomotives, longer rail lines, more steamboats, and more automatic machinery were echoed by the slightly shocked engineers who came to the United States from Great Britain and France to view the achievements of this period.

This is an epic which deserves to be studied and recognized—not alone as a story within the history of technology but as a central thread in American history. In the perspective of the general historian, does not this define the era with far more justice than the westward-moving wagon trains, the Age of Jackson, or the battles over the tariff? Indeed, these episodes, which still constitute the warp and woof of traditional history, are understandable only in terms of the technology which rebuilt the floor under the pontificating senators even as they declaimed and which shaped and reshaped the tools required to conquer a continent and to erect a variant civilization.

The grandeur of this story is perhaps the most telling force behind the overemphasis upon republican technology. It introduces the historian of technology to the too frequent practice of the general historian in lopping off the colonial period from serious consideration and beginning his account of American history with the Revolution.[34] It is a practice not to be encouraged in either sphere. In its own right, and as the root of later growth, colonial technology demands study by those qualified to evaluate it.

Even the most elementary questions about the chronology of American technology immediately introduce the necessity of understanding the European chronology. In fact, every probe into American technology requires attention to comparable, contemporary European patterns. This not only provides a necessary standard of evaluation; it acknowledges a process which remained fundamental throughout the period—the transfer of technology from Europe to America.

The transit of civilization from Europe to America is one of the established elements of American history. Although it has probably been more acknowledged than studied in all of its aspects, it is a part of the general historian's outlook. The transfer of laws, governmental institutions, architecture, science, religion, and attitudes is so familiar

34. Carl Bridenbaugh, "The Neglected First Half of American History," *American Historical Review*, 52 (1948), 506–17.

that we think of much narrative history in these terms. Curiously, the transfer of technology has not had equivalent recognition. At the scholarly level it is now receiving some study, but at the popular level there is a conflicting image of American whittling boys inventing their way—through cotton gins, steamboats, mass production, telegraphs, and vulcanized rubber—from the colonial world of hand production to the new world of machine production. This picture is not without truth, but it is not a satisfactory vehicle for crossing the great technological divide or, indeed, for taking any extended trip. The transfer of technology is a more fundamental factor within the context of technological history. In the broader sweep of general American history, it is an essential element which must take its place beside the other aspects of civilization which were transferred. Study may, in fact, reveal that nothing imported from Europe was so important to the success of the colonizing endeavors or to the growth of the new nation as its techniques for making and doing things.

As with other elements in the transit of civilization, the transfer of technology was a continuing process which early provoked a counter-current carrying American innovations and alterations in the opposite direction. The westward current flowed increasingly as American needs grew, but before 1850 it had ebbed considerably in those lines of conspicuous American attainment. The eastward current was continuing to rise at the end of the period.

The entire process requires detailed investigation, but a preliminary view of the major current westward suggests that it was primarily a matter of the immigration of artisans, mechanics, and engineers with the required skills and techniques. This was the ancient means of acquiring new technologies, as Elizabeth had done in importing Flemish weavers. In early America, it was supplemented by manuals and how-to-do-it books, which sold very well, and ultimately by textbooks and treatises. It was further enriched by visits of Americans to Europe for specific investigation and for training. Time after time, however, those who visited Europe to discover new techniques decided that the safest approach was to bring back Europeans with the skill to do what they wanted done. This immigration was overwhelmingly British, seasoned regionally in the colonial period by Germans and Dutch, in the Revolutionary era by French, and at the end of the period by Germans.

A generalization frequently made by Americans was that British technology was practical and successful while French technology was elegant *but* theoretical. American experience usually sustained the implications of this view, although their reliance upon the French was strong in military engineering, in some related civil engineering, and in engineering education. This was true in large part because the United States fought its first two wars against Great Britain, thus barring British military engineering during the periods of greatest need. In drug and fine chemical production, and in certain other lines where the scientific element was significant, American reliance upon Continental Europe was strong in the early nineteenth century. When American academic men, such as Jacob Bigelow, Thomas Cooper, and James Cutbush, sought to apply science to technology, they reached more and more for French assistance. The evidence suggests, however, that in the textile mill and the machine shop the British remained the dominant European influence.

A contrary view is suggested in studies which apply the methods of intellectual history to the problem of technological transfer, but the methods are inapplicable and the conclusions false. Timoshenko's fine history of the strength of materials can be used only as a genealogical survey of the key writings around which present theory evolved.[35] It has no relevance to eighteenth- and nineteenth-century American practice in this area and very little relevance to British practice. The foundation theory was largely Continental and heavily French, but it was not influential in America until much later. More specifically misdirected is Shaw's demonstration that modern libraries hold proportionately more French than British engineering works published before 1830.[36] This statistical measure, of course, means little unless we know when the books were acquired, by whom, and—more pointedly—who used them. In all probability, the French books were acquired at a later date and ultimately used effectively by those who sought to find better theoretical and scientific foundations for technology. There is little indication that they were as important to practicing American mechanics and engineers at the time of publication as their numbers in the libraries of the present suggest.

Such studies do not challenge the view of Britain as America's primary European reliance in building and extending her technology, but they do suggest that some methods of study must be regarded dubiously. The "intellectual thread" approach may not serve the history of technology as effectively as it does other fields. Statistical measures, of course, must always be controlled carefully, but perhaps they require

35. Stephen P. Timoshenko, *History of Strength of Materials* (N. Y., 1953).
36. Ralph R. Shaw, *Engineering Books Available in America prior to 1830* (N. Y., 1933).

special attention in intellectual approaches to technology. Shaw's book-counting method seems a classic example of being misled by "non-significant survivals." [37]

The same hazards must be guarded against in using some of the largest concentrations of writing about technology which seem to offer so much promise; for example, patents and patent-related collections, government reports, engineering reports, manuals, and college textbooks. The question must continuously be asked whether the surviving written record tells us the most important things about the technology we study, a subject which was itself not fundamentally an intellectual or verbal construction. Must not the focus be upon the things built and the men who built them? This would include all of the direct evidence on and about the functioning technology and all of the evidence—much of it informal, scattered, and difficult to assess—about the men involved.

Some of the questions to be asked are suggested by the key problems about early American technology which are now attracting competent attention. Perhaps the most dramatic of these is the development of the "American system" of manufacturing by interchangeable parts. This has long been celebrated as an American achievement, but the written record, so far uncovered, is as limited in specifics on this development as it is at many of the other critical points in the history of technology. The focal question in most of the writing on this subject has been whether the successful accomplishment sprang, more or less full grown, from the brow of Eli Whitney. It was answered in the affirmative by most of the early writers but in the negative by Woodbury and Sawyer, who then move on to larger considerations.[38]

This single question carries with it a heavy freight. It implies the assumption that the great question about technology is: at what points and by what process did it move from one level of development to a higher and more complex level? It also carries the generic answer that advance has come by individual, inventive ingenuity. Yet neither of these propositions is self-evident. Because they are so generally accepted, it is essential that efforts be made to discover precisely what happened in the critical episodes. The specific, written information will always be inadequate, so related questions which can be answered must be pursued. It may turn out that they, after all, are the more important.

37. Daniel J. Boorstin, Anglo-American Historical Conference, London, July 10, 1965.
38. Robert S. Woodbury, "The Legend of Eli Whitney," *Technology and Culture*, 1 (1960), 235–51; John E. Sawyer, "The Social Basis of the American System of Manufacturing," *Journal of Economic History*, 14 (1954), 361–79.

In the case of interchangeable parts, one must know just what Bentham, Brunel, and Honoré Blanc did. What was their machinery? (This question is easily answered for the Brunel-Bentham efforts in making blocks for the Royal Navy.) In what places and how widely were Blanc's efforts to manufacture muskets and Bentham's 1793 patent known? What else of this sort was in the air? How did these and other contemporary efforts compare with Whitney's? Were his solutions, especially his use of jigs, different? How did the chronology of Whitney's accomplishments compare with the chronology of Simeon North's and the government armories' applications of the idea of interchangeable parts?

Merely to ask such questions raises some doubt about the comparative significance of a great, naked idea—such as interchangeable parts—and its technological fulfillment. The fulfillment is never instantaneous; in this case it was clearly a story of long growth, development, and extension. Inventive ingenuity was a continuing factor along the route. Historians must certainly use their maximum insight to discover all that can be known about this process.

However, they may have to take answers where they are available rather than where they would like to find them. John Fitch left a full and introspective record of his steamboat-building endeavors which appears to answer the questions of greatest moment. Yet the historian no sooner encounters Fitch's unqualified assertion that the concept of the steam engine came fresh to his mind, with absolutely no knowledge of previous engines, than he realizes that it does not matter much whether this was true or not. For the history of technology, the important thing is the account of the process by which Fitch's ideas of engines were gradually expanded as he built one after another, applying them through different linkages and different propulsive schemes to setting a boat in motion. Some of this he did mentally and some in three-dimensional form—always changing, adapting, and rebuilding as one element or another proved unsatisfactory. Throughout his manuscripts he reveals—almost as an allegory—a conflict between himself, as a man of naked ideas, and his partner, Henry Voight, as a brilliant and intuitive mechanic who translated dreams into working reality.

More often invention is chronicled only in the most formal records. The heroic, stroke-of-genius view of technology is given significant support by the greatest body of available sources on technological specifics —the patent records. The patent system is both a product and a cause of the heroic view of invention. For this and for a variety of other reasons technology continues to be viewed too often as a story of invention. The words "technology" and "invention" appear in some histories virtually as synonyms.

The difficulties in defining invention are monumental, but the concept is valid not only as a part of the technological process but as an element of all creative work: aesthetic, literary, and scientific. Even the patentability requirements of originality, novelty, and utility are usable restrictions, within limits. At the same time, mechanical invention and technological innovation have emerged from recent study as complicated processes, exceedingly difficult to tie to one man or moment of time.

To begin with, technology, like science, has an internal life with an integrity of its own which determines the fruitful routes of its own change and adaptation. At any given moment some "inventions" are possible and some are simply impossible until more elements have been added to the complex. The routes of change actually followed depend upon environmental circumstances, including political, social, and economic factors, and upon the impress of individual personality. Yet, at each point of development, certain changes and adaptations grow logically out of the state of the technology. This has been well demonstrated in Robert K. Merton's study of the prominence of "multiples" in scientific discovery and invention, but it is an old story to the patent attorney.[39] Simultaneous invention and multiple invention or reinvention are continuing parts of history.

Moreover, it may be useful to assume that each technological complex operates, on a small scale, within bounds which Thomas S. Kuhn, writing of science, has called a set of paradigms.[40] The basic ingredients for a new set are always present some time before they are put into working order. Thus we might project the steamboat story: all the elements of a technically successful steamboat were at hand before one was built. They were even put together in a steamboat before technical success was achieved and certainly before the revolution in water transportation was accomplished. The same thing can be said of machine manufacture on the basis of interchangeable parts, or the cotton gin, or the reaper, or the electric telegraph. If this is so, we may have to limit the identification of inventors to very specific items (such as the Whitney gin or the Danforth throstle), and abandon efforts to tag the inventor of the steamboat or of interchangeable parts. Yet such eponyms are more a part of the history of technology—especially of

39. Robert K. Merton, "Singletons and Multiples in Scientific Discovery: A Chapter in the Sociology of Science," *American Philosophical Society, Proceedings,* 105 (1961), 470–86.

40. Thomas S. Kuhn, *The Structure of Scientific Revolutions* (Chicago, 1962).

early American technology—than of most other areas of human creativity.

Is it not necessary for the historian to come to terms with the internal life of technology before he seeks to assign title as inventor or to confer other accolades? This requires an understanding of the details of the technology under study. It requires an end to prejudice against the "hardware historian." It requires an effort to see through the eyes and feel through the hands of the craftsman and mechanic. The social relations of technology must not be neglected; they represent the historian's highest goal, but they are attainable only after the historian has developed a direct understanding of the men and their works.

One of the great questions that might yield to the central study of technology is the extent to which its internal character is deterministic. It is clear that at each stage of development, new possibilities are opened. When, before it was possible to travel in steam vehicles, Oliver Evans spoke of the exhilaration to be anticipated, he was not thinking of monetary profit at all. He was participating in the fulfillment of an unfolding technology. Norris built more powerful locomotives not merely to make money but perhaps more basically from a great human urge to do everything that developing means permit man to do. Were they so inner-directed that they failed to exercise needful restraint in moving as fast as they did toward dependence upon machines?

Perhaps technology was not so much a tool or a means as it was an experience—a satisfying emotional experience. When it became possible to make thread and cloth by machine, they were so made; when boats, trains, and mills could be driven by steam, they were so driven. These things could be accomplished only to the extent that economic needs and social attitudes permitted; but is it not possible that the more elemental force was within the technology itself? It is an idea often denied.

The men who constructed the elements of early American technology were themselves a part of it. Their words reflect an emotional satisfaction in reaching forward with each improvement. It is doubtful that the central role of technology in American history will ever be apprehended until this drive is appreciated. Its recognition alone will constitute a response to recent critiques emphasizing the evil results of technology— a response in the form of an explanation, not necessarily a denial.

The greatest need is to stand at the center of the technology—on the inside looking out. Instead, we have usually looked at technology from the outside: through the eyes of science, economics, political reflections, social results, or literary antagonisms. There is no telling what related factors and forces will appear once the historian develops his insights from the center; it has hardly been tried. As Daniel J. Boorstin put it, the history of technology is indeed one of the "dark continents" of historiography.[41]

Once the external view of technology is modified and the intensity of concentration on invention is relaxed, a number of pervasive themes within technology come to mind, some of them not even progressive in nature. One of these is the spread and conflict of different cultural traditions within the same technology. For example, Baron Hermelin wrote that iron production at the end of the colonial period was dominated in some regions by German methods, in some by Flemish, and in others by English.[42] If this was so, a fine comparative study in differences and effects is in order. Similarly, the influx of foreign artisans in glass production continued throughout the entire period. Some of the effects appear in the catalogs of glassware collectors, but no comparative study of the technology has been attempted. Again, Ewbank suggested that Philadelphia fire engines followed French and German models while New York adhered to British patterns. Why should this have been so, and how did it influence development? [43]

Another comparative pattern is offered in the divergence between the southern shovel plow and the northern wooden plow; why the difference? A different sort of comparison is the lengthy competition between the Rhode Island and the Waltham systems of cotton textile production. This has been more noted by historians, but the voluminous records have never been adequately studied.

Major questions in almost endless number can be identified within the context of the interrelationships of technology and American society. Did educational patterns promote the acceptance of technological improvements as foreigners believed; and, in turn, did the new technology push American education along already determined routes? Was the traditional secrecy of the mechanic's "little black book" minimized by the openness of American society and the unusual mobility enjoyed by craftsmen and mechanics? [44] How in each episode did the several governments influence and how were they influenced by technology? Especially intriguing is a question suggested by Eugene S. Ferguson: did the Americans speed their technological development by a "doctrine

41. Early American Technology Conference.
42. Samuel Gustaf Hermelin, *Report about the Mines in the United States of America, 1783* (Phila., 1931), 63–65.
43. Thomas Ewbank, A *Descriptive and Historical Account of Hydraulic and Other Machines* (14th edn., N. Y., 1858), 343.
44. Lawrence W. Towner, Early American Technology Conference.

of imperfectability?" Were they more ready than the Europeans to recognize that imperfection in machine parts was not merely acceptable but inevitable, and, if so, what in their background encouraged this difference? [45]

Among other pervasive themes that hold keys to the "Americanness" of American technology is the wooden age of our technological history. Here the Americans diverged sharply from European example in the use of material and, unexpectedly, in other directions as well. Architectural historians, agricultural historians, maritime historians, and historians of other aspects of technology have described portions of this story, but its dimensions have not yet been measured. Wood was used not only for houses and monumental buildings but for canal locks, for canals themselves, for road surfaces (the famous plank roads), for steamboats, for steam engine framing, for railroad ties (in place of stone blocks), for bridges, and even for compasses and mathematical instruments.

This reliance upon wood subsided from its peak before mid-century, but it had many results and ramifications and it continued to differentiate America from western Europe. It brought the Americans acknowledged leadership in wood-working tools, marked especially by the use of the muley saw, the circular saw, and the elegant American axe.[46] By promoting rapid obsolescence and replacement, it promoted the adoption of improved techniques or of techniques that were merely different. It may have facilitated the spread of machine production; handmade brass clockworks were followed by machine-made wooden works and then, in turn, by machine-made brass works. It offered a model which the Russians, conspicuously, found more to their taste than European models when they sought railroad engineers with solutions to problems of large distances and few resources other than wood. It played a large part in conquering the American continent (and theirs) with limited labor and capital.

The wooden age was closely related to another pervasive theme: labor-saving machinery. This concern may be stated most positively in terms of attitude, because the early nineteenth-century Americans wrote often of the merits and desirability of labor-saving machines. European observers acknowledged that the American view of this subject differed from theirs. Habakkuk, on the other hand, has recently found reason

45. Early American Technology Conference.
46. For a stimulating suggestion for comparative studies of tools, see the comment by Whitfield J. Bell in Walter Muir Whitehill, Wendell D. Garrett, and Jane N. Garrett, *The Arts in Early American History: Needs and Opportunities for Study* (Chapel Hill, 1965), 19.

to question whether American labor was scarce in the sense believed and, if it was, whether labor-saving devices were the best answer.[47] The Americans did not have such doubts, yet they sometimes recognized that their capital was almost equally scarce. If solutions were what contemporaries believed them to be (reliance on machinery, cheap materials, standardization, poor finish, and lower levels of skill in labor), these characteristics are very significant in technological history.

When European commentators sought the pervasive characteristics of American technology, they often noted a "character of magnitude" plus a battery of differentiating American attitudes. All reported the fixation upon labor-saving machinery, resulting, as one account put it, in "the universal application of machinery with a rapidity that is altogether unprecedented." [48] The lack of fine finish and highly skilled work was related to the American's pride "in not remaining over long at any particular occupation, and being able to turn his hand to some dozen different pursuits in the course of his life." [49] Such restlessness, another commentator believed, inverted European attitudes toward changing techniques: "In England it is said, a custom so old 'must be right;' in America, that a custom so old 'must be wrong,' and needs revolution or change." [50] A French observer added that in America "one learns to appreciate the value of time: they employ it, while we use it." Even more perceptively, he noticed the manner in which American attitudes toward technology were woven into the fabric of their most cherished ideals; "Steam, with the Americans, is an eminently national element, adapted to their character, their manners, their habits, and their necessities. With them it is applied as much to extend their liberty as to augment their physical welfare. . . . The American seems to consider the words democracy, liberalism, and railroads as synonymous terms." [51]

Study of the chronological history, the internal nature, and the pervasive characteristics of early American technology are fundamental needs at this stage. All require a continuing sensitivity to the social relations of technology. No historian has to be reminded that the social, economic, and political relationships cannot be added as a gloss on top

47. Habakkuk, *American and British Technology*, 8, 21–25.
48. Publisher's advertisement in Strickland *et al.*, *Public Works*, n.p.
49. Joseph Whitworth and George Wallis, *The Industry of the United States* (London, 1854), 2.
50. John Richards, A *Treatise on the Construction and Operation of Wood-Working Machines* (London, 1872), 125.
51. Guillaume Tell Poussin, *Chemins de Fer Américains* (Paris, 1836), xvi; *The United States: Its Power and Progress* (London, 1851), 345, 371.

of the basic technological history; they are an integral part of the story. The big questions about social history must be kept in mind even to get the most out of an investigation of the shape of a screw.

The immediate difficulty is that the chronology and general character of early American technology can only be established through the detailed study of one specific technological episode after another. The great need is to get inside the men, their tools, and their works. Biographical studies of men will be useful, but despite the central importance of the human element, they are probably less valuable than "biographies" of crafts, of the various mechanical and engineering developments, and of the institutions within which technology was developed and assimilated. Unfortunately, this detailed study cannot be successfully pursued until the general questions have first been answered! This is a familiar dilemma. Tentative generalizations must be accepted in order to permit the scholar pursuing detailed research to ask the proper questions. Then, as more satisfying details become available, the generalizations can be improved.

The importance of the questions to be asked cannot be overemphasized because the historian, like the inventor, will find little significant information except that for which he has searched. He must be prepared to ask the large questions of small episodes. He must also be aware of the questions asked by society—especially the rising number of critiques of technology in our own day. The opportunities are enormous and the principal qualification is an open mind stocked with good questions. Since we are not yet entirely sure what are the "right" questions or the "right" approaches, it is doubly necessary that no doors be closed and that the insights of all who have looked in this direction be sought. Most important of all is the enthusiasm of the early American craftsman, mechanic, and engineer. Unless the historian can catch some of that spirit he will render a better service by studying in some other field.

The ultimate objective is to raise technology to its proper place within the context of early American history. It belongs very close to the center as an expression and a fulfillment of the American experience.

A BIBLIOGRAPHY
OF EARLY AMERICAN
TECHNOLOGY

by Brooke Hindle

I. INTRODUCTION

This bibliography offers a personal reaction to the available writings on early American technology. It has been conceived in the thought that such a tour by a general historian with a special interest in the history of technology would accomplish two purposes. It should identify the most fruitful descriptive, analytic, and synthetic works on technology in America before 1850, whether written before that date or since. At the same time, its organization and tenor should serve to sketch the terrain of technology through this period and to indicate the sort of work that has been done in the various sectors.

It is severely limited in length and therefore highly selective—but more selective in some quarters than in others. More marginal works are included in areas of interest where little else is to be found. The articles included are conceived to be of special significance, beyond that attached to many of the books noticed. Further, works relating to the central story of technological development itself are given more attention than those dealing with its many relationships—its backward and forward linkages.

The primary organization represents a division of the whole realm of technology into those elements which seem most logical in the context of early American history even though they are not necessarily the categories preferred by the best scholars today. In addition, brief attention is given to a few of the special relationships of technology.

II. GUIDES AND SOURCES

The best monographs of the recent past can be expected to provide critical assistance in locating source materials; and older works, many of which did not follow modern canons in presenting their bibliographical material, often left their trails clearly marked. Thus, many of the works cited below fill this office. In addition, important help is available in a great number of guides and bibliographies in which technology is considered as a minor element. More important in determining the shape of this essay and more fundamental for those who seek aid in approaching early American technology are a handful of separate bibliographies.

Paramount among them is Eugene S. Ferguson, "Contributions to Bibliography in the History of Technology," published serially in *Technology and Culture*, 3 (1962), 73–84, 167–74, 298–306; 4 (1963), 318–30; 5 (1964), 416–34, 578–94; 6 (1965), 99–107, and soon to be issued under separate cover. This is a survey of the sources by one of the best equipped of the currently active scholars, and it is distinguished by qualitative evaluations and comments throughout. Although embracing the entire range of history, it is most complete for the nineteenth-century United States and perhaps most perceptive on mechanical engineering. It is especially sensitive to guides and to the approaches which ought to be made to the various areas of technology by the research scholar. It is a great resource. The Society for the History of Technology has not only encouraged the production of Ferguson's bibliographies but some of its members have contributed their aid. In addition, the Society's Bibliography Committee has begun an annual "Current Bibliography in the History of Technology," *Technology and Culture*, 5 (1964), 138–48; 6 (1965), 346–74.

A much longer run of annual bibliographies in which technology has always been an integral element is the "Critical Bibliography of the History of Science and Its Cultural Influences," in *Isis*, the organ of the History of Science Society. Both the attention accorded to technology and the critical character of this bibliography are likely to increase in the future. Another annual bibliography of occasional value is the "Articles in American Studies," appearing in *American Quarterly*. This is a listing of interdisciplinary works; items in which technology is related to another field or fields are noted under "Science and Technology."

Directly pertinent are two of the bibliographies published as a result of earlier conferences in the "Needs and Opportunities" series sponsored by the Institute of Early American History and Culture. Whitfield

J. Bell, Jr., *Early American Science: Needs and Opportunities for Study* (Williamsburg, 1955), covers a closely allied story which frequently overlaps and always provides related guidance for those who study technology. Mr. Bell is preparing a second edition which will include work done since 1955. More recent is the annotated bibliography prepared by Wendell D. and Jane N. Garrett in Walter Muir Whitehill, *The Arts in Early American History: Needs and Opportunities for Study* (Chapel Hill, 1965). This has a particular pertinence because of the need to approach the arts anew and restudy them from the viewpoint of technology. That was not the position from which the Garretts' bibliography was constructed, but much that it contains can be pressed into this service.

Among the sources for the history of technology a certain primacy must be recognized in the artifacts or three-dimensional objects preserved from the period studied. Both the products of technology and the machines and tools used to produce them are important. The historian of technology must view the objects of technology in much the same light as the historian of art views the paintings whose history he studies. In order to emphasize this necessity and to provide some of the guidance required, Lucius F. Ellsworth has prepared for this book a separate Directory of Artifact Collections.

The central significance of three-dimensional source materials cannot obscure the greater utility of the conventional reliances of the historian. Only the smallest portion of the objects of technology have been preserved and, even if they were more extensive, the information they present would remain limited. More condensed information is available through the shorthand of language and through two-dimensional drawings.

In referring to the written record, the historian traditionally accords manuscripts an especially honored place, imagining that they bring the closest access to the minds of men of the past. Often however, especially in technology, clearer pictures are left in organized printed treatises and reports. The colonial craftsman and the republican mechanic were not as given to scribbling as the clergyman and the politician, and their papers were not as frequently preserved. Few were as introspective as John Fitch, and when educated engineers wrote journals, as did Benjamin Henry Latrobe, they filled much of them with other matters. Nevertheless, correspondence becomes increasingly valuable in the nineteenth century, and business records and other manuscript materials become more frequent.

The accessibility of manuscripts has been greatly improved since the publication of Philip M. Hamer, ed., *Guide to Archives and Manuscripts in the United States* (New Haven, 1961), although it can be relied upon only for its positive statements—not for what it fails to mention. Its statements on the primary libraries are basically those supplied by the librarians. The largest manuscript repositories often have printed guides to their collections. Sometimes typescript guides to sections are available at the libraries, and informed librarians can always supply help not offered in either guides or card catalogs.

Among the more valuable collections are those of the American Philosophical Society in Philadelphia, which not only preserves its own archives and correspondence from the 1760's but, in addition, holds separate collections of importance for technology. These include the Peale-Sellers Collection and the newly acquired records of the Carpenters' Company of Philadelphia. The Franklin Institute in Philadelphia also preserves its own seminal records and other collections.

The Library of Congress was surveyed from the viewpoint of technology by Nathan Reingold, "Manuscript Resources for the History of Science and Technology in the Library of Congress," *Library of Congress, Quarterly Journal of Current Acquisitions*, 17 (1960), 161–69. Among pertinent collections are the John Fitch Papers, the William Thornton Papers, the R. Hoe and Company records, and the Samuel F. B. Morse Papers. The smaller but sometimes useful collections of the Museum of History and Technology of the Smithsonian Institution have not been similarly sketched.

Business records, remaining very largely in manuscript form, are found in private hands and in a variety of libraries. Most used by economic historians, they often contain invaluable data for the historian of technology. A good guide to the records and to works about them is Henrietta M. Larson, *Materials for the Study of American Business History and Suggestions for Their Use* (Cambridge, Mass., 1948). Probably the largest collection of holdings is in the Baker Library of the Harvard Business School; it includes Pepperell, Isaac Briggs, and Boston Manufacturing Company manuscripts. Yale University has Whitney manuscripts; Brown University those of George Corliss; and the University of Pennsylvania possesses the papers of the Samuel Wetherill firm. The Eleutherian Mills-Hagley Foundation in Wilmington began with a great nucleus of papers of the various Du Pont enterprises and has been adding to them.

The great manuscript repositories in Boston, New York, Baltimore, and Philadelphia all contain extensive holdings. The Massachusetts

Historical Society, for example, has a large collection of manuscripts relating to the brass and copper works of Paul Revere and to the later Joseph Revere and Company. The New-York Historical Society has accounts and letters of Harmon Hendrix, supplier of nonferrous metals. The Maryland Historical Society recently acquired the Latrobe Papers and the Historical Society of Pennsylvania the Tench Coxe Papers; the latter, however, are not yet open to use.

Many less obviously important libraries contain individual collections of value. Thus, the Stevens Institute of Technology in Hoboken, New Jersey, holds the John and Edwin A. Stevens Papers, and Cooper Union in New York has manuscripts of Peter Cooper and Abram S. Hewitt. The Library Company of Philadelphia holds John Fitch materials, the Essex Institute in Salem, Massachusetts, the Nathan Read Papers, the Library of the DeGolyer Foundation, Dallas, the records of the Baldwin Locomotive Works and the Charles B. Stuart drawings, and the Transportation Library of the University of Michigan, Oliver Evans materials. In its Joseph Downs Collection of manuscripts and microfilms, the Winterthur Museum has sizable and well-indexed materials relating primarily to crafts and craftsmen.

Governmental archives relating to technology in the colonial period are valuable at all levels but low in yield and frequently disappointing. In the national period, they become enormously important—city, county, state, and national. Some of the states have done a good job of publishing their colonial archives, but even there, examination of the unpublished manuscripts can produce surprising results. The archival accumulation of the nineteenth century has passed the possibility of publication. State and city reports on specific problems, such as canal construction and water supply systems, are drawn from official records. The state archives can often be consulted directly, but when city archives have not been destroyed, they are usually stored out of reach and out of knowledge. The great body of state and local archival material remains very difficult to use.

The National Archives present many categories of materials directly pertinent to the study of technology, the most generally important of which are probably the Patent Office Records. Nathan Reingold has surveyed these holdings in "U.S. Patent Office Records as Sources for the History of Invention and Technological Property," *Technology and Culture*, 1 (1960), 156–67, and on a broader base, "The National Archives and the History of Science in America," *Isis*, 46 (1955), 22–28. Of the many other useful papers in the National Archives, only selected record groups have been provided with preliminary inventories. The total of significant holdings is very great, and all are distinctly more accessible than most state and local archives.

Published governmental records abound. The large collections of state and national legislative records, laws, and administrative reports contain very occasional sections of great importance to technology. Separately published surveys and specific reports are often very valuable; some of these are noted under the appropriate topical headings below.

Among the good libraries of eighteenth- and early nineteenth-century works on technology, the Library Company of Philadelphia is outstanding; it is especially rich in American and British works directed to the average man and to the mechanic. The A. Lawrence Kocher Collection of Colonial Williamsburg is a library on building practices, town planning, gardening, and taste in colonial America—notably strong in manuals for builders and gardeners. A descriptive catalog is planned in the near future. The Oscar Guttman Collection of the Eleutherian Mills Historical Library is a unique library on explosives; some 500 volumes in French, German, Italian, and English. The Thayer School of Engineering Library at Dartmouth College contains Sylvanus Thayer's personal collection of books and journals. One of the best working libraries of nineteenth-century engineering books is the William Barclay Parsons Collection of the New York Public Library.

The whole range of periodical literature constitutes another category of materials, sources which have hardly been exploited. Newspapers retain value from their first appearance, but the character of information to be extracted from them alters considerably during this period of time. Colonial papers are valuable not only for news but also for essays bearing on technology, for letters, and for advertisements. Microcopies of several of the colonial papers are now available, but the only satisfactory index is Lester J. Cappon and Stella M. Duff, eds., *Virginia Gazette Index*, 1736–1780 (Williamsburg, 1950). With the Revolution, an abrupt change occurred; many newspapers became dailies, most became absorbed with politics, and they surrendered their interest in essays and topical discussion to the magazines. Yet their news and their advertisements continue to reflect much of technology. Unfortunately, the indexing of this corpus has not proceeded far; the *New York Tribune* index (1841–1850+) covers at least a segment of the early period.

The journals of all the early learned societies professed interest in technology, usually under the rubric, "American Improvement." The earliest volumes printed more items on technology; the *Transactions* (1771–1850+) of the American Philosophical Society (abbreviated APS in subsequent references) offer such items as Owen Biddle's file machine (1771) and Benjamin Latrobe's report on steam engines (1803). Similar in character were the *Memoirs* (1785–1850+) of the American Academy of Arts and Sciences; more specialized, but still presenting technological items, were the *Memoirs* (1808), of the Philadelphia Society for Promoting Agriculture, and the *Transactions* (1815–25) of the Literary and Philosophical Society of New York.

Interest in technology grew in such late colonial magazines as the *American Magazine* (1769) and the *Pennsylvania Magazine* (1775–76), continued in the *American Museum* (1787–92) and the *Massachusetts Magazine* (1789–96), and declined with the more literary magazines such as the *Port Folio* (1810–27). Another species of magazine which sought to report events introduced much technology, perhaps the best example being *Niles' Weekly Register* (1811–49). The more commercial and encyclopedic periodicals became even more useful: *Hunt's Merchants' Magazine and Commercial Review* (1839–50+) and *De Bow's Review* (1846–50+).

In only a small group of periodicals did technology become a center of interest. Most important was the *Emporium of Arts and Sciences* (1812–14) which, while edited by John Redman Coxe, was a collection of undigested snips and pieces, much of it from European sources. When Thomas Cooper became editor, it carried genuinely synthetic appraisals of areas of technology, such as iron production and steam engines. Less valuable and ambitious were *The Useful Cabinet* (1808) and the *Archives of Useful Knowledge* (1810–13). Benjamin Silliman's *American Journal of Science* (1819–45) was directed toward basic sciences but also to "their applications to the arts and to every useful service." In fact, items important to technology appeared with some regularity.

By all measures, the most important technological journal was the *Journal of the Franklin Institute* (1826–50+), which far transcended the limited significance of its predecessor, the *American Mechanic's Magazine* (1825–26). It has a unique value before 1836 because of its record of patents granted in that period, for the originals, along with all supporting evidence, were lost in the Patent Office fire. It also greatly extended the influence of the Institute itself in technological instruction. A deeper value lies in its reflection of Institute activities in reviewing inventions and techniques, and in presenting original articles and articles freshly translated from French and German and not otherwise available in the United States.

From the time of the success of the Franklin Institute's *Journal*, other journals seeking to convey information to the mechanic began to appear, many of them short-lived. Among them were: *Albion* (1822–50+), *American Repertory of Arts, Science and Manufactures* (1840–42), *Farmer and Mechanic* (1844–50+), *Mechanics' Advocate* (1846–48), *Mechanics' Magazine and Register of Inventions and Improvements* (1833–37), *New York State Mechanic: A Journal of the Manual Arts, Trades, and Manufactures* (1841–43), and *Quarterly Journal of Agriculture, Mechanics, and Manufactures* (1834–35). The earliest journals in specific industries appeared in railroading: *Rail Road Journal* (1832–50+) and *Railway Times* (1849–50+).

Published travel accounts offer a rich although generally low-yield source of direct reflections upon technology. These range from specific descriptions and evaluations of machinery to comments upon the social, economic, and political consequences of the state of technology. The density of such materials in colonial accounts is remarkably slight compared with reports of trips taken in the republican period, beginning perhaps with Johann David Schoepf, *Travels in the Confederation*, 1783–1784, trans. by Alfred J. Morrison, 2 vols. (Philadelphia, 1911). In the 1790's several travel accounts display these interests; one of particular utility is Henry Wansey, *The Journal of an Excursion to the United States of North America in the Summer of 1794* (Salisbury, 1796). A second is the Duc de la Rochefoucauld-Liancourt's *Travels Through the United States of North America, 1795, 1796, 1797*, 4 vols. (2nd edn., London, 1800); David J. Brandenburg is preparing a new—and for the first time a complete—translation which will be published by the Institute of Early American History and Culture. There is a great concentration of pertinent accounts in the 1820's, among them Isaac Holmes, *An Account of the United States of America* (London, 1823) and *Baron Klinkowstrom's America, 1818–1820*, trans. by Franklin D. Scott (Evanston, 1952). The reverse current of American travelers commenting on European technology is also of value; a thin account of this type is Zachariah Allen, *The Practical Tourist, or Sketches of the State of the Useful Arts . . . in Great Britain, France, and Holland*, 2 vols. (Providence, 1832).

III. SURVEYS AND STUDIES

A. *General Surveys*

The larger the generalization in any field of history, the more questionable is its validity in application to details, and it becomes still less certain when erected upon inadequate foundations. For the history of technology, there is not yet a sufficiently secure collection of limited-range studies to make possible satisfying general syntheses. However, it is not possible to contemplate any field without seeking at least an interim conceptual survey of the whole, and those who have attempted such syntheses are therefore the more to be thanked because of the inadequate building blocks available to them. Some of the most penetrating insights about the over-all course of technology are found in limited-range studies, but the general survey does fill an essential role.

Two multivolumed surveys of the entire range of technology have appeared recently. The five-volume *History of Technology*, edited by Charles Singer, E. J. Holmyard, A. R. Hall, and Trevor I. Williams (London, 1954–58), seeks to cover all technology to 1900. Its most conspicuous omissions are military technology and any genuine effort to relate technology to general history. A compound of topical chapters within large chronological units, it is well organized, although the individual contributions are inescapably of uneven value. Volumes III and IV provide the background against which American technology developed. Insofar as such a thing is possible, T. K. Derry and Trevor I. Williams, *A Short History of Technology* (Oxford, 1961), represents a condensation of these volumes. Only the first volume of Maurice Daumas, *Histoire Générale des Techniques* (Paris, 1962), has appeared, but the editor projects four volumes of a similar, composite character. The initial volume reaches only the Middle Ages but gives indications that the series may serve as a corrective to British emphases and that it may sustain a stronger sense of direction than Singer's survey.

Of the current textbook-type syntheses, probably the most generally useful are two by James Kip Finch, *Engineering and Western Civilization* (New York, 1951) and *The Story of Engineering* (Garden City, 1960). Engineering is not identical with technology, but the coverage here is broad; in the nineteenth century, the American story becomes dominant. In Richard S. Kirby, Sidney Withington, Arthur B. Darling, and Frederick G. Kilgour, *Engineering in History* (N. Y., 1956), two engineers and two historians combine in the authorship, but the result is more selective and less unified than Finch's. Briefer and less American in emphasis is Robert J. Forbes, *Man the Maker* (N. Y., 1950, 1958).

Limited in chronology largely to the early American period are A. Wolf, *A History of Science, Technology and Philosophy in the 16th and 17th Centuries* (London, 1935; N. Y., 1950, 1959) and *A History of Science, Technology and Philosophy in the 18th Century* (N. Y., 1939, 1961). Technology, in these volumes, forms a minor but considerable element. Abbot Payson Usher, A *History of Mechanical Inventions* (Cambridge, Mass., 1929, 1954; Boston, 1959), is a classic, a pioneer survey of one of the key threads in Western technology.

Among earlier surveys, the encyclopedias have been justly recognized for their attention to the technology of their own day. First among them is Diderot's great *Encyclopédie*; the flavor of its technological plates have been made accessible recently in Charles C. Gillispie, ed., *A Diderot Pictorial Encyclopedia of Trades and Industry*, 2 vols. (N. Y., 1959). Other French encyclopedias are also of value, although less directly pertinent than several British works, including the *Encyclopaedia Britannica* which was first reprinted in the United States under the abbreviated title, *Encyclopaedia*, 18 vols. (Philadelphia, 1798). Most extensively useful of the British encyclopedias which went into early American editions is Abraham Rees, *Cyclopaedia*, 39 vols. text + 6 vols. plates (Philadelphia, 1810–24). More limited in scope is Andrew Ure, *Dictionary of Arts, Manufactures, and Mines* (N. Y., 1842), but even the later English editions of this work carried American material.

B. *American Surveys*

American technology before 1850 has so far been no better provided with satisfying syntheses than has general Western technology. The most recent and hopeful effort was John W. Oliver, *History of American Technology* (N. Y., 1956), which does provide detailed information plus an organizational framework. Its facts, however, put together with great patriotic verve, reflect inadequate response to the important questions. Although journalistic and one-tracked, Roger Burlingame, *March of the Iron Men: A Social History of Union through Invention* (N. Y., 1938), remains more helpful. Dirk J. Struik, *Yankee Science in the Making* (Boston, 1948), is better read but marked by Marxist overtones and by the thesis that the streams of science and technology finally came together in the founding of M.I.T. (1865). Waldemar Kaempffert, ed., *A Popular History of American Invention*, 2 vols. (N. Y., 1924), is a cooperative coverage of much of American technology, but more effective as a celebration than as a survey. Although not written as a survey of technology, A. Hunter Dupree, *Science in the Federal Government* (Cambridge, Mass., 1957), presents an excellent review of all the technology related to the federal government.

Early surveys often tended toward a biographical model, following and paralleling the vast success of Samuel Smiles with his seriatim works on English mechanics and engineers. The first was Henry Howe, *Memoirs of the Most Eminent American Mechanics* (N. Y., 1842), popularly written but based significantly upon various mechanical journals of the day. Charles B. Stuart, *Lives and Works of Civil and Military Engineers of America* (N. Y., 1871), George Iles, *Leading American Inventors* (N. Y., 1912), and even Richard S. Kirby, ed., *Inventors and Engineers of Old New Haven* (New Haven, 1939), follow the pattern of unrelated biography.

Manufacturing includes only a portion of technology, but surveys of manufacturing usually do comprehend the largest and most significant portion. This is conspicuously true of two works which cover almost exactly the period embraced in this bibliography. The better is J. Leander Bishop, *A History of American Manufactures from 1608 to 1860*, 3 vols. (Phila., 1861–68). This is a mine of information rather than a source of interpretation, carrying a great many undocumented but accurate facts arranged primarily in chronological order. In addition, appendices present individual and company biographies. Victor S. Clark, *History of Manufactures in the United States, 1607–1860* (Washington, 1916), despite the nearly identical title, is very different in character. In keeping with its place in the Carnegie series, it maintains an economic historian's outlook, interprets much more generally, and follows modern scholarly canons, but it is less likely to supply specific, hidden details.

Other synthetic works have more limited utility. Albert S. Bolles, *Industrial History of the United States* (Norwich, Conn., 1879), gives much attention to process and product, and Carroll D. Wright, *The Industrial Evolution of the United States* (N. Y., 1902), also admits technological elements. Both are fundamentally economic histories, as is Malcolm Keir, ed., *Manufacturing: A Volume of Industries of America* (N. Y., 1928).

Many local histories contain valuable, sometimes otherwise unattainable, information on technology; their utility in this connection is likely to be greater if written before 1910. Especially helpful, although sometimes inaccurate, are John Thomas Scharf and Thompson Westcott, *History of Philadelphia, 1609–1884*, 3 vols. (Phila., 1884), and Scharf, *History of Delaware, 1609–1888*, 2 vols. (Phila., 1888). Although disorganized, James M. Swank, *Progressive Pennsylvania* (Phila., 1908), is made useful by its concern for mining and manufactures. Manufacturing towns are chronicled in Alonzo Lewis and James R. Newhall, *History of Lynn* (Boston, 1865), and C. E. Patter, *The History of Manchester* (Manchester, 1856). Constance McLaughlin Green, *History of Naugatuck, Connecticut* (New Haven, 1949), is alive to technology. In a class by itself is I. N. Phelps Stokes, *Iconography of Manhattan Island*, 6 vols. (N. Y., 1895–1926).

Another category of writings seeks specifically to survey local technology, principally manufacturing. Outstanding are Edwin T. Freedley, *Philadelphia and Its Manufactures* (Phila., 1859), and L. R. Trumbull, *A History of Industrial Paterson* (Paterson, 1882). Even the glossy vanity books are useful: for example, J. D. Van Slyck, *New England Manufacturers and Manufactories,* 2 vols. (Boston, 1879), and Orra L. Stone, *History of Massachusetts Industries,* 4 vols. (Boston, 1930). William B. Weeden, *Economic and Social History of New England, 1620–1789,* 2 vols. (Boston, 1890), is especially responsive to technology in the later chapters. But the more recent economic histories usually focus primarily on matters other than technology: Isaac Lippincott, *A History of Manufactures in the Ohio Valley to the Year 1860* (Chicago, 1914); Vera Shlakman, *Economic History of a Factory Town: A Study of Chicopee, Massachusetts* (Northampton, Mass., 1935); and Thomas Russell Smith, *The Cotton Textile Industry of Fall River, Massachusetts* (N. Y., 1944). For New Jersey, Harry B. Weiss, in some cases with other authors, has written a long series of pamphlets concerned with techniques and physical remains. Many are mentioned in the ensuing pages; the most general is Harry B. and Grace M. Weiss, *Forgotten Mills of Early New Jersey: Oil, Plaster, Bark, Indigo, Fanning, Tilt, Rolling and Slitting Mills, Nail and Screw Making* (Trenton, 1960).

Unusually precise surveys of technology are available in the encyclopedias and dictionaries of the arts, published for many years in Europe and finally, at the very end of the period, issued in the United States. Several British works were republished in the United States, and where American additions can be identified they are significant but do not constitute reviews of American technology. One of the first to provide a fresh review of American developments was *Appleton's Dictionary of Machines, Mechanics, Engine-Work, and Engineering,* 2 vols. (N. Y., 1852). It was put together with the assistance of numerous American engineers, with reliance upon Patent Office drawings and specifications, and with European works for guidance. Narrower in focus and much less original was the third volume of *Putnam's Home Cyclopedia,* issued as T. Antisell, *Hand-book of the Useful Arts* (N. Y., 1852), while Spencer F. Baird, ed., *Iconographic Encyclopaedia of Science, Literature, and Art,* 6 vols. (N. Y., 1851–52), was primarily extractive. In a different category was Edward Hazen, *The Panorama of Professions and Trades* (Phila., 1837), an elementary guide for juveniles selecting a trade.

Industrial exhibitions offered another opportunity for surveying American technology and, ultimately, for measuring it against a world background. The most important local exhibitions were those of the Franklin Institute, beginning in 1824. Typical of the survey possibilities is the *Report of the Twenty-Second Exhibition of American Manufactures Held in the City of Philadelphia from the 19th to the 30th of October, Inclusive, 1852 by the Franklin Institute* [Phila., 1853]. Many surveys were set in motion by the Great Exhibition of 1851 in London. Among them, two of the American reports have survey characteristics: Charles T. Rodgers, *American Superiority at the World's Fair* (Phila., 1852), and Benjamin P. Johnson, *Great Exhibition of the Industry of All Nations, 1851* (Albany, 1852). Even more pertinent were the reports of English commissions sent to the United States to appraise American technology. The most general and accessible of these is Sir Joseph Whitworth and George Wallis, *The Industry of the United States* (London, 1854). Summaries of the impact of American technology are contained in Monte A. Calvert, American Technology at World Fairs, 1851–1876 (M.A. thesis, University of Delaware, 1962), and Merle Curti, "America at the World Fairs, 1851–1893," *American Historical Review*, 55 (1950), 833–56.

Finally, the many federal government reports constitute another series of surveys of American technology. Hamilton's "Report on Manufactures," together with its background, is made available in Arthur Harrison Cole, ed., *Industrial and Commercial Correspondence of Alexander Hamilton, Anticipating His Report on Manufactures* (Chicago, 1938). Tench Coxe, who helped with this report, also wrote voluminously on manufactures, from *Observations on the Agriculture, Manufactures and Commerce of the United States* (N. Y., 1789) to his own government reports, of which that on the Census of 1810 is most useful, *A Statement of Arts and Manufactures ... for the Year 1810* (Washington, 1814). Two reports of Albert Gallatin are fundamental: *Report of the Secretary of the Treasury on the Subject of Public Roads and Canals* (Washington, 1808), and "Report on Manufactures, 1810," *American State Papers: Finance Vol. II* (Washington, 1832), 425–39. Still more comprehensive is [Louis McLane], U. S. Treasury Department, *Documents Relating to the Manufactures in the United States*, 2 vols. (Washington, 1833). Other surveys, especially of smaller compass, abound in colonial, state, and federal publications.

C. Agriculture and Food Processing

The technology of agriculture was of fundamental importance throughout the entire early American period. Not only did agriculture remain the largest economic pursuit, but its technology is of intrinsic significance. Historians of technology have given limited attention to this field, but economic historians and agricultural historians have written about it extensively. Recent studies of agricultural technology are especially promising, although farming and milling machinery receive more attention than hand tools, soil chemistry, animal husbandry, and other compartments of "doing things" in agriculture. Yet, both the subject matter and the writings related to agriculture are enormous if all aspects of all of agriculture plus lumbering, whaling, and fishing are included.

There is no survey of agricultural technology, but the two Carnegie Institution volumes include careful attention to technology and together cover the field: Percy W. Bidwell and John I. Falconer, *History of Agriculture in the Northern United States, 1620–1860* (Washington, 1925), and Lewis C. Gray and E. K. Thompson, *History of Agriculture in the Southern United States to 1860*, 2 vols. (Washington, 1933). Useful, too, is the brief work of Everett E. Edwards, "American Agriculture—The First Hundred Years," U. S. Department of Agriculture, *Yearbook of Agriculture, 1940* (Washington, 1941).

Among classic printed reviews, only a handful can be mentioned. The first American book on the subject was Jared Eliot, *Essays Upon Field Husbandry in New England and Other Papers, 1748–1762*, ed. by Harry J. Carman and Rexford G. Tugwell (N. Y., 1934). Other significant and revealing colonial accounts are: *American Husbandry* [London, 1775], ed. by Harry J. Carman (N. Y., 1939), and Carl R. Woodward, ed., *Ploughs and Politics: Charles Read of New Jersey and His Notes on Agriculture, 1715–1774* (New Brunswick, 1941). Republican pieces include John Beale Bordley, *A Summary View of the Courses of Crops in the Husbandry of England and Maryland* (Phila., 1784), and Richard Peters, *Agricultural Enquiries on Plaister of Paris* (Phila., 1797). A new corner was turned in Edmund Ruffin, *An Essay on Calcareous Manures* [1832], ed. by J. Carlyle Sitterson (Cambridge, Mass., 1961). Among mounting numbers of volumes, a handbook helps: Henry Colman, *Agriculture and Rural Economy* (Boston, 1849).

Such works as these, both reviewing techniques and advocating changes, demonstrate much interest in plows and seed drills but less perhaps than in rotation and fertilizing. The background of the latter is set in C. A. Browne, *A Source Book of Agricultural Chemistry* (Waltham, 1944), and the most influential study of a segment of the problem is Avery O. Craven, *Soil Exhaustion as a Factor in the Agricultural History of Virginia and Maryland, 1606–1860* (Urbana, Ill., 1925).

The central story of the development of agricultural machinery has produced several excellent studies, most of them dealing largely with the nineteenth century. Worth recalling is Thomas Jefferson, "The Description of a Mouldboard of the Least Resistance," APS, *Transactions*, 4 (1799), 313–22. R. L. Ardrey, *American Agricultural Implements: A Review of Invention and Development in the Agricultural Implement Industry of the United States* (Chicago, 1894), presents a broad coverage of hand tools as well as machines, but largely in terms of patents and without much reference to the earliest period. The best biography of the most celebrated inventor is William T. Hutchinson, *Cyrus Hall McCormick*, 2 vols. (N. Y., 1930, 1936). More sharply focused is Edward C. Kendall, *John Deere's Steel Plow* (U. S. National Museum, *Bulletin*, No. 218 [Washington, 1959], pp. 15–25). Leo Rogin, *The Introduction of Farm Machinery in Its Relation to the Productivity of Labor in the United States during the Nineteenth Century* (Berkeley, 1931), is directly interested in the technology. More economically centered is Hadly W. Quaintance, *The Influence of Farm Machinery on Production and Labor* (N. Y., 1904). A fine balanced study of technology and its consequences is Reynold M. Wik, *Steam Power on the American Farm* (Phila., 1953); however, only a small part of it relates to the early period.

Of the machinery used to process agricultural products, flour mills are the most important and the most written about. Such surveys as exist are either overly general or tend to neglect the colonial period; John Storck and Walter D. Teague, *Flour for Man's Bread: A History of Milling* (Minneapolis, 1952), covers all history but with special reference to the American scene, and Charles Byron Kuhlmann, *The Development of the Flour-Milling Industry in the United States* (Boston and N. Y., 1929), is brief on the early period. Brief but with good descriptions and views of the machinery are Harry B. and Grace M. Weiss, *The Early Snuff Mills of New Jersey* (Trenton, 1962), and Harry B. Weiss and Robert J. Sim, *The Early Grist and Flouring Mills of New Jersey* (Trenton, 1956). A local study of superior scholarship is Peter C. Welsh, "The Brandywine Mills: A Chronicle of Industry, 1763–1816," *Delaware History*, 7 (1956), 17–36.

The role of Oliver Evans is so important in the development of flour milling that the key publication becomes his *The Young Mill-Wright and Miller's Guide* (Phila., 1795). Also helpful is the translation, *Guide du Meunier et du Constructeur de Moulins* (Paris, 1830), valuable for the notes by the translator, Phillippe M. N. Benoit, who later expanded them and published them with the same title but under his own name (Paris, 1863). Greville and Dorothy Bathe's biography, *Oliver Evans: A Chronicle of Early American Engineering* (Phila., 1935), is a very careful study with good factual information and detailed evaluations but lacking in flow and perspective. A much reprinted handbook gives a good picture of practice at mid-century: William Carter Hughes, *The American Miller, and Millwright's Assistant* (Detroit, 1850).

Of pursuits related to agriculture, lumbering and its technology is particularly interesting but little studied. Weak on technology are both James Elliott Defebaugh, *History of the Lumber Industry of America*, 2 vols. (Chicago, 1906), and Robert G. Albion, *Forests and Sea Power* (Cambridge, Mass., 1926). A little more to the point is F. E. Coyne, *The Development of the Cooperage Industry in the United States* (Chicago, 1940). Although English, John Richards, *A Treatise on the Construction and Operation of Wood-Working Machines: Including a History of the Origin and Progress of the Manufacture of Wood-Working Machinery* (London, 1872), covers American inventions and methods in lumbering and sawing.

Colonial experiments in timber and naval-stores production usually failed for technical reasons, but the treatment of them is primarily political in Eleanor L. Lord, *Industrial Experiments in the British Colonies of North America* (Baltimore, 1898), and W. A. Knittle, *Early Eighteenth Century Palatine Emigration: A British Redemptioner Project to Manufacture Naval Stores* (Phila., 1937).

The technological aspects of fishing, whaling, and even livestock raising are of equally great importance. A considerable literature includes brief attention as a part of many books but little concentrated study limited to these phases. Beginnings are offered in R. A. Clemen, *The American Livestock and Meat Industry* (N. Y., 1923), A. Starbuck, *History of the American Whale Fishery from Its Earliest Inception to the Year 1876* (Waltham, 1876), and Raymond McFarland, *A History of the New England Fisheries* (N. Y., 1911).

D. Mining and Metals

From the beginning there was a consciousness of extensive mineral wealth in America, and mining, especially iron mining, became an early part of the economy. Mining of other metals developed slowly, and coal mining lagged because the Americans did not quickly follow England's lead in using coal and coke for iron ore reduction. Despite the quantity of works on iron mining and iron production, there is little on the American story that approaches the quality of recent studies of the general history of mining and metals.

Specific backdrops to American mining are offered in H. R. Schubert, *History of the British Iron and Steel Industry from c. 450 to A.D. 1775* (London, 1957), and Theodore A. Wertime, *The Coming of the Age of Steel* (Leiden, 1961). Still deeper background studies are Leslie Aitchison, *A History of Metals*, 2 vols. (London, 1960), and Cyril S. Smith, *A History of Metallography* (Chicago, 1960).

There is no satisfactory American survey although Thomas A. Rickard makes the attempt: *History of American Mining* (Phila., 1932). Despite its inadequacies, the best general picture remains James M. Swank, *History of the Manufacture of Iron in all Ages and Particularly in the United States from Colonial Times to 1891* (2nd edn., Phila., 1892). Even more poorly organized and less scholarly, but useful, particularly in the later chapters, is John B. Pearse, *A Concise History of the Iron Manufacture of the American Colonies up to the Revolution, and of Pennsylvania until the Present Time* (Phila., 1876). The Metallurgical Society of the American Institute of Mining, Metallurgical and Petroleum Engineers recently issued in book form a *History of Iron and Steelmaking in the United States* (N. Y., 1961). The articles were written by men who are not historians but they sometimes provide useful leads; all the essays had previously appeared in the *Journal of Metals*.

Fortunately, some of the major figures in iron production left helpful commentaries. Peter Hasenclever did not very satisfactorily explain the collapse of his extensive industrial empire in New Jersey and New York, but he set forth some of the details in *The Remarkable Case of Peter Hasenclever* (London, 1773). The questions are not cleared up in the thin biography, Adolf Hasenclever, *Peter Hasenclever, aus Remscheid* (Gotha, 1922). Although not primarily technical, the survey of the Swedish appraiser is good: Samuel Gustaf Hermelin, *Report about the Mines in the United States of America, 1783* (Phila., 1931). Abram S. Hewitt was not a careful historian, but some of his own recollections are important in *A Century of Mining and Metallurgy in the United States* (Phila., 1876) and *On the Statistics and Geography of the Production of Iron* (N. Y., 1856). A sort of contemporary survey is J. P. Lesley, *The Iron Manufacturer's Guide to the Furnaces, Forges and Rolling Mills of the United States* (N. Y., 1859).

There are a surprising number of studies of local iron production which vary in period and in quality. Pennsylvania has received the greatest concentration of attention, the key study being Arthur C. Bining, *Pennsylvania Iron Manufacture in the Eighteenth Century* (Harrisburg, 1938). Of some use is the site-by-site commentary, *Forges and Furnaces in the Province of Pennsylvania* (Phila., 1914). Louis C.

Hunter is especially probing in his article, "Influence of the Market upon Technique in the Iron Industry of Western Pennsylvania to 1860," *Journal of Economic and Business History*, 1 (1929), 241–81. Similar in character to his more general work is James M. Swank, *Introduction to a History of Ironmaking and Coal Mining in Pennsylvania* (Phila., 1878). The most recent study is Joseph E. Walker's *Hopewell Village: A Social and Economic History of an Iron-Making Community* (Phila., 1966). On New Jersey, there is a superior site-by-site commentary: Charles S. Boyer, *Early Forges and Furnaces in New Jersey* (Phila., 1931). Arthur D. Pierce is useful in both *Iron in the Pines* (New Brunswick, 1957) and *Family Empire in Jersey Iron* (New Brunswick, 1964). There are also two somewhat ephemeral pieces: James S. Brown, *Allaire's Lost Empire* (Freehold, N. J., 1958) and Robert J. Sim and Harry B. Weiss, *Charcoal-Burning in New Jersey* (Trenton, 1955).

Among the sparser writings about the technology of iron production in other colonies and states, early Massachusetts has been favored. E. N. Hartley, *Ironworks on the Saugus* (Norman, Okla., 1957), by the historian of the restoration of the seventeenth-century enterprise, rests in part on archaeology and study of physical technology. For Ohio, there is Frank H. Rowe, *History of the Iron and Steel Industry in Scioto County* (Columbus, 1938), and for Virginia the more substantial but still not sufficiently technological work of Kathleen Bruce, *Virginia Iron Manufacture in the Slave Era* (N. Y., 1931). An excellent new study is James D. Norris, *Frontier Iron: The Maramec Iron Works, 1826–1876* (Madison, Wis., 1964).

On processes, one of the best brief technical accounts is William H. Harrison, "The First Rolling Mill in America," American Society of Mechanical Engineers, *Transactions*, 2 (1881), 104–7. Much more extensive is the practical handbook, Frederick Overman, *The Manufacture of Steel* (Phila., 1851). Although European in origin, Peter Tunner, *A Treatise on Roll-Turning for the Manufacture of Iron* (N. Y., 1869), was translated and adapted by an American (John B. Pearce), and it is relevant to mid-century practices.

Production and work in other metals never assumed any of the proportions of the iron industry. There is one survey: Walter Renton Ingalls, *Lead and Zinc in the United States: Comprising an Economic History of the Mining and Smelting of the Metals* (N. Y., 1908); an earlier, narrower work is Henry R. Schoolcraft, *A View of the Lead Mines of Missouri* (N. Y., 1819). Benjamin Henry Latrobe, *American Copper Mines* (n.p., n.d. [1800?]), is a brief pamphlet on the Schuyler copper mine; Harry B. and Grace M. Weiss, *The Old Copper Mines of New Jersey* (Trenton, 1963), offers a recent and broader treatment. William G. Lathrop, *The Brass Industry in Connecticut* (Shelton, Conn., 1909), is thin, with only occasional attention to technology.

E. *Military*

The enormous role of military effort in the development of American technology deserves attention of a magnitude it has not yet begun to receive. This may be the result of the American delusion that we have not been a military people, but the neglect of the field is not a peculiarly American phenomenon, as the parallel omissions of Singer's large *History of Technology* demonstrate. The force of the military impulse can be conveniently dissipated by scattering the effects among the appropriate topical categories: all of the developments under warship construction, submarines, and propulsion can be placed under naval architecture or transportation; arms and interchangeable parts under manufacturing techniques; gunpowder production under chemical technology; Army exploration, cartography, and river improvement under engineering; and wind and current charts under science and technology. Indeed, the careful analysis of most of these developments requires that they be so considered. However, historians must recognize the role of government support (principally by the federal government) in encouraging several sectors of technology through the military services or for military purposes. It is an inspiring story of the greatest significance.

In the strict sense of military engineering, the major effort to supply the needed techniques began with the Revolution in the assumption of unwonted tasks by Americans: the importation, translation, and study of treatises, and the use of European engineers. This is a part of the story sketched briefly in I. Bernard Cohen, "Science and the Revolution," *Technology Review*, 47 (1945), 367–68, 374–88. The long-continued dependence on European military writings appears in Sidney Forman, "Early American Military Engineering Books," *Military Engineering*, 36 (1954), 93–95. There are biographies of some of the Europeans who brought to America the needed skill: Albert H. Heusser, *The Forgotten General: Robert Erskine* (Paterson, 1928); Miecislaus Haiman, *Kosciuszko in the American Revolution* (N. Y., 1943); and Elizabeth S. Kite, *Brigadier General Louis Lebegue Duportail* (Baltimore, 1933).

The projection of these beginnings through the development of the Military Academy and the Engineer Corps has called forth piecemeal recognition. Although severely limited, perhaps the most convenient account of West Point is Sidney Forman, *West Point: A History of the United States Military Academy* (N. Y., 1950). William Couper's biography, *Claudius Crozet* (Charlottesville, 1936), documents continuing reliance upon Europeans. So do publications which served as textbooks, such as Louis Tousard, *American Artillerist's Companion*, 3 vols. (N. Y., 1809); this describes cannon manufacture and testing as well as techniques of emplacement and firing. The Army finally broke free of dependence upon the republication of European tracts with Dennis Hart Mahan's *A Treatise on Field Fortification* (N. Y., 1836) and his *An Elementary Course of Civil Engineering* (N. Y., 1837), both of them pioneering efforts. Some of the extended influence of the Army engineers is described in W. Stull Holt, *The Office of the Chief of Engineers of the Army: Its Non-Military History, Activities, and Organization* (Baltimore, 1923); William H. Goetzman, *Army Exploration in the American West, 1803–63* (New Haven, 1959), on the topographical engineers; and Forest G. Hill, *Roads, Rails, and Waterways: The Army Engineers and Early Transportation* (Norman, Okla., 1957), the best of these three studies.

Even when compared with the great influence of military engineering upon American transportation technology, the influence of arms production on almost all sectors of technology can scarcely be exaggerated. One of the great colonial achievements in technology was in precisely this field—the Pennsylvania rifle. There are several studies of this critical American development but all primarily from the viewpoint of gun collectors and fanciers. Even the most recent, Henry J. Kauffman, *The Pennsylvania-Kentucky Rifle* (Harrisburg, 1960), has just a minor interest in technology; Francis Jordan, Jr., *The Life of William Henry of Lancaster, Pa., 1729–1786* (Lancaster, 1910), is a poor work but contains important information on one of the most prominent of the colonial and Revolutionary gunmakers.

The greatest achievement to come out of arms production, of course, was interchangeable parts or the "American system of manufacturing." This has had recognition equivalent to its importance and now seems to be receiving the study it deserves. Robert S. Woodbury in "The Legend of Eli Whitney," *Technology and Culture*, 1 (1960), 235–51, assaults as a myth the idea that Whitney "discovered" interchangeable parts. John E. Sawyer in "The Social Basis of the American System of Manufacturing," *Journal of Economic History*, 14 (1954), 361–79, broadens the base of understanding. Both men have spoken elsewhere of French practice as the source of interchangeability but have not yet published the evidence.

The biographies of Whitney present the old view of this development but add information on many related points of technology:
Jeannette Mirsky and Allan Nevins, *The World of Eli Whitney* (N. Y.,
1952), and Constance McLaughlin Green, *Eli Whitney and the Birth
of American Technology* (Boston, 1956). The basic source biography
is Denison Olmsted, *Memoir of Eli Whitney* (New Haven, 1846).

Indeed, it appears probable that the bare concept of interchangeability was less important than its workable fulfillment and its extension. This owed much to Whitney but also to other private manufacturers, who introduced it almost coincidentally, and to the government armories. Elements of this development are presented in Joseph
W. Roe, "Interchangeable Manufacture," Newcomen Society, *Transactions*, 17 (1937), 165–74; Charles H. Fitch, "The Rise of a Mechanical Ideal," *Magazine of American History*, 2 (1884), 516–27;
and K. R. Gilbert, "The Ames Recessing Machine: A Survivor of the
Original Enfield Rifle Machinery," *Technology and Culture*, 4 (1963),
207–11. A good survey with strength in technology is Felicia J. Deyrup,
Arms Makers of the Connecticut Valley (Northampton, 1948). A
different sort of survey is Charles B. Norton, *American Inventions and
Improvements in Breechloading Small Arms, Heavy Ordnance, Machine Guns, Magazine Arms* (Springfield, Mass., 1880). S. N. D. and
Ralph H. North, *Simeon North, First Official Pistol Maker of the
United States* (Concord, N. H., 1913), is a filiopietistic biography
of one of Whitney's contemporary claimants to the interchangeability principle. Some guidance to the very fundamental contributions of the government armories is presented in *The National Armories:
A Review of the System of Superintendency, Civil and Military,
Particularly with Reference to Economy, and General Management
at the Springfield Armory* (2nd edn., Springfield, Mass., 1852).

The invention of the Colt revolver was another technological achieve-
ment with wide repercussions; its production was an extension of the
American system. Most recent of many writings on Colt is a showy
book for collectors but with an interest in technology: William B.
Edwards, *The Story of Colt's Revolver: The Biography of Col. Samuel
Colt* (Harrisburg, 1953).

In fact, a large proportion of all publications on arms are written
by or for collectors. They are not ideally suited to the needs of the
historian of technology, but they are often excellent in detail and
can be put to very good use. Among the best are those of Claud E.
Fuller: *Springfield Muzzle-Loading Shoulder Arms: A Description of
the Flint Lock Muskets, Musketoons, Rifles, Carbines and Special
Models from 1795 to 1865* (N. Y., 1930) and *The Whitney Firearms*

(Huntington, W. Va., 1946). A. Merwyn Carey, *American Firearms Makers* (N. Y., 1953), is an annotated directory. Best of James E. Hicks' works is *U. S. Military Firearms, 1776–1956* (La Canada, Calif., 1962). He has also written on swords: *Nathan Starr (The First Official Sword Maker)* (Mt. Vernon, N. Y., 1940). In a different category is Harold L. Peterson, *The American Sword, 1775–1945* (New Hope, Pa., 1954); Peterson's *Arms and Armor in Colonial America, 1526–1783* (Harrisburg, 1956) is the best available survey.

Like gunpowder production, warship construction and naval technology seem best considered later in this bibliography, but a few items are of the same character as the foregoing. The initial ideas on submarines, for example, were military in character. Especially pertinent are David Bushnell, "General Principles and Construction of a Submarine Vessel," APS, *Transactions*, 4 (1799), 303–12, and Robert Fulton, *Torpedo War and Submarine Explosions* (N. Y., 1810). Worthy of even more attention is Capt. Alfred Mordecai, *Report on Experiments on Gunpowder made at the Washington Arsenal in 1843 and 1844* (Washington, 1845).

F. *Civil Engineering and Transportation*

The term civil engineering appeared late but was long used to differentiate non-military work from military engineering; by the mid-nineteenth century it still included what is now called mechanical engineering. It was not used in the early colonial period although men who went by different titles performed many of the tasks later assumed by the civil engineer. In the American Republic, the civil engineer became absorbed primarily in laying out and building the network of internal improvements—chiefly canals and railroads. The whole of transportation was not his responsibility and he had other tasks not related to transportation, but, in the United States, civil engineering is largely a question of transportation development.

1. *General Syntheses.*—There are a number of contemporary surveys of civil engineering works, called more often interior communications or the transportation system. The Americans did not produce the numerous, expensive picture books celebrating engineering achievements in the way the British did. In fact, they were less effective in compiling surveys of any sort than were visiting Europeans. The best of these is David Stevenson, *Sketch of the Civil Engineering of North America* (London, 1838); a knowledgeable Scot, he presents a remarkably well-paced view of harbors, lake and river improvements,

steamboats, building methods, canals, roads, bridges, railroads, waterworks, and lighthouses. More limited in scope but more Germanically ponderous is the work of the Austrian, Franz Anton von Gerstner, *Die Innern Communicationen der Vereinigten Staaten von Nordamerica*, 2 vols. (Vienna, 1842–43). By far the most prolific were the French. Guillaume Tell Poussin's three enthusiastic works should be regarded as a unit: *Travaux d'Améliorations Intérieures* (Paris, 1834), the *Atlas* (Paris, 1834) to accompany it, and *Chemins de Fer Américains* (Paris, 1836). On river boats alone, an excellent survey is Jean Baptiste Marestier, *Mémoire sur les Bateaux à Vapeur des États-Unis* (Paris, 1824); it has been partially translated into English by Sidney Withington as *Memoir on Steamboats* (Mystic, Conn., 1959). Less technologically oriented are Henri Stucklé, *Voies de Communication aux États-Unis* (Paris, 1847), and Michel Chevalier, *Histoire et Description des Voies de Communication aux États-Unis* (Paris, 1840). All of the Europeans evinced a friendly and laudatory attitude, but the French in particular seemed quite incapable of comprehending how the Americans had succeeded so well.

American surveys were less specific on the technology. One of the earliest and best organized was [Mathew Carey], *A Connected View of the Whole Internal Navigation of the United States* (Phila., 1826); it is based on clippings and additional material, some of it relating to engineering, still preserved in the Library Company of Philadelphia. Other reviews are H. S. Tanner, *A Description of the Canals and Rail Roads of the United States* (N. Y., 1840), and Henry V. Poor, *History of the Railroads and Canals of the United States* (N. Y., 1860).

Of later surveys, J. L. Ringwalt, *Development of Transportation Systems in the United States* (Phila., 1888), is concerned with technology. Two recent economic histories are outstanding, both in the "Economic History of the United States Series." Curtis P. Nettels, *The Emergence of a National Economy: 1775–1815* (N. Y., 1962), handles competently many technological details. George Rogers Taylor, *The Transportation Revolution: 1815–1860* (N. Y., 1951), is similarly very helpful on bibliography but, in addition, gives proper recognition to the vast influence of the technological changes of these years, not only on the economy but on all of American life.

2. *The Engineers.*—An unusual recent study offers an excellent approach to the engineers and their works: Daniel H. Calhoun, *The American Civil Engineer: Origins and Conflict* (Cambridge, Mass., 1960). He describes the development of a profession, identifying the

major figures from 1815 to mid-century and sketching their training and role. His story is related primarily to the construction of the transportation system, and he examines especially the rise of centers of professional training.

Many of the engineers have been recognized and celebrated; they are found in general biographical dictionaries. They are perceptively noted in Stuart's *Lives and Works of Civil and Military Engineers*. There are various smaller collections of sketches: [James Kip Finch], *Early Columbia Engineers* (N. Y., 1929); Richard S. Kirby, "Some Early American Civil Engineers and Surveyors," Connecticut Society of Civil Engineers, *Papers and Transactions*, 1930, pp. 26–47; and Joseph Jackson, *Early Philadelphia Architects and Engineers* (Phila., 1922).

The early engineers were frequently both architects and engineers, and biographical studies tend to emphasize their architecture. Benjamin Henry Latrobe is favored with a rounded biography, based upon careful research, by Talbot Hamlin, *Benjamin Henry Latrobe* (N. Y., 1955). Several of Latrobe's reports are noted elsewhere in this bibliography; his most general publication is his *Journal... from 1796 to 1820* (N. Y., 1905). Two of Latrobe's outstanding students have biographies: H. M. Pierce Gallagher, *Robert Mills: Architect of the Washington Monument, 1781–1855* (N. Y., 1935), and Agnes A. Gilchrist, *William Strickland, Architect and Engineer, 1788–1854* (Phila., 1950). Both are best on the architectural side. Strickland's own writings are more helpful: *Reports on Canals, Railways, Roads, and Other Subjects* (Phila., 1826), *Internal Improvement* (Phila., 1825), and (with Edward H. Gill and Henry R. Campbell), *Public Works of the United States of America* (London, 1841). One well-focused recent study is available only on microfilm: Frederick K. Abbott, The Role of the Civil Engineer in Internal Improvements: The Contributions of the Two Loammi Baldwins, Father and Son, 1776–1838 (Ph.D. diss., Columbia, 1952, on Ann Arbor microfilm).

3. *Surveying.*—One aspect of civil engineering that was very much older than the emergence of a specific profession was surveying—an aspect that remained central to the establishment of the nineteenth-century network of internal transportation. From the earliest colonization, this art required attention. At the lowest level, it was a question only of the use of compasses and chains; at the more sophisticated level of boundary determination, it required astronomical fixes. From an early date, surveyors' manuals imported from Britain presented the

basic techniques. Later they were published in America and, finally, many were written here. Some American examples are: Robert Gibson, *A Treatise of Practical Surveying* (5th edn., Phila., 1789); John Gummere, *A Treatise on Surveying* (Phila., 1820, 1828, 1836); and Samuel Moore, *An Accurate System of Surveying* (Litchfield, 1796).

There are no useful histories of surveying, although some of the works on surveying instruments offer help (see pages 72–73). Closely related, too, is the large field of cartography. Biographies of some of the notable surveyors are pertinent: P. Lee Phillips, *Notes on the Life and Works of Bernard Romans* (Deland, Fla., 1924); Brooke Hindle, *David Rittenhouse* (Princeton, 1964); and Catharine Van C. Matthews, *Andrew Ellicott* (N. Y., 1908). Also important for Ellicott as a surveyor is his *Journal* (Phila., 1803).

Although the state geological surveys seem a little too peripheral for historians of technology, the United States Coast Survey does represent a central achievement in surveying techniques. The remaining records are in the National Archives, although some are available in the collection published by the first director, Ferdinand Rudolph Hassler: *Principal Documents Relating to the Survey of the Coast of the United States since 1816* (N. Y., 1834). There is also Florian Cajori's biography, *The Chequered Career of Ferdinand Rudolph Hassler* (Boston, 1929). Merle Odgers' biography of the second director, *Alexander Dallas Bache* (Phila., 1947), is less satisfactory; Nathan Reingold is preparing a new one. Although primarily a legal study, some help is offered in William D. Pattison, *Beginnings of the American Rectangular Land Survey System, 1784–1800* (Chicago, 1957).

4. *Ships and Shipbuilding.*—Shipbuilding in many ways represented the most complex technological enterprise entered into during the colonial period. Because it stood as a composite of most of the crafts of a shipbuilding town, it might be regarded as a product of manufacturing as well as the source of the primary means of transportation. Ships have been accorded great attention: in connection with maritime and naval history, as an aspect of economic history, and by enthusiasts of a similar character to the collectors of antiques and old guns. But neither the technology of shipbuilding nor that of design has been studied as it should be.

The best surveys are of the ships rather than of the processes of building them, but when well done, they reflect back much insight into shipbuilding. Perhaps the leading surveys of this sort are those of Howard I. Chapelle; his two large works are *The History of American*

Sailing Ships (N. Y., 1935) and *The History of the American Sailing Navy* (N. Y., 1949). Of the same caliber is his *The Baltimore Clipper, Its Origin and Development* (Salem, 1930). Chapelle expresses strong opinions on technological matters and on many others. A less scholarly enthusiast was John H. Morrison, once a shipbuilder himself. His *History of American Steam Navigation* (N. Y., 1903), *History of New York Ship Yards* (N. Y., 1909), and *Iron and Steel Hull Steam Vessels of the United States, 1825–1905* (reprint from *Scientific American Supplement*, 21 [1905]) are folksy catalogs with often rare information. Among almost endless ship books, two of the best are Arthur H. Clark, *The Clipper Ship Era* (N. Y., 1911), and David B. Tyler, *Steam Conquers the Atlantic* (N. Y., 1939). Still more helpful for technology is the latter author's *The American Clyde: A History of Iron and Steel Shipbuilding on the Delaware from 1840 to World War I* (Newark, Del., 1958).

A few broad-gauged studies of local maritime history are especially apt. Two outstanding works are by general historians who are ship enthusiasts as well: Samuel E. Morison, *The Maritime History of Massachusetts, 1783–1860* (Boston, 1921), and Robert G. Albion, *The Rise of New York Port (1815–60)* (N. Y., 1939). Also relevant is the latter's *Square Riggers on Schedule* (Princeton, 1938). For Maine, there is William Hutchinson, *The Maritime History of Maine: Three Centuries of Shipbuilding and Seafaring* (N. Y., 1948).

The Americans did not early produce their own manuals or treatises on shipbuilding; to the extent that they used any, they relied on several British works. Joshua Humphreys had a copy of Mungo Murray, *A Treatise on Shipbuilding and Navigation* (2nd edn., London, 1764), with its translations of Bouquer and Duhamel. Isaac Taylor, *The Ship, or Sketches of the Vessels of Various Countries with the Manner of Building and Navigating Them* (Phila., 1854), is popular and general but gives some insight into methods. More helpful are two big, glossy books by Charles B. Stuart, himself an engineer: *The Naval and Mail Steamers of the United States* (N. Y., 1853) and *The Naval Dry Docks of the United States* (N. Y., 1852). They are detailed even to the point of presenting drawings and specifications of bilge pumps. Occasionally detailed pieces appeared with significant information: for example, *Report of the President and Trustees of the Ship Timber Bending Co.* (N. Y., 1854) describes methods of artificially bending framing timbers to the required forms.

Finally, just after mid-century a remarkable work appeared which was filled with insights not obtainable elsewhere: John W. Griffiths,

Treatise on Marine and Naval Architecture, or Theory and Practice Blended in Ship Building (N. Y., 1851). This large undertaking is based on the belief that European treatises did not help much in the United States, because of different terms in use, because they were not fundamentally intended for merchant shipbuilding, and because they were not sufficiently adapted to the knowledge and talents of the operative mechanic. The result is very helpful to the historian.

5. *Steam and River Boats.*—The great rivers of America, so much more satisfactory for navigation than many of the European rivers, were a stimulus to invention and enterprise from an early point. One of the great colonial developments was the Durham boat, a fine, low-draft carrier of bulk cargo. Only a sketchy beginning in the study of boat building technology is offered in J. A. Anderson, *Navigation of the Upper Delaware* (Trenton, 1913). Another species of freight carrier is better treated in Leland D. Baldwin, *The Keelboat Age on Western Waters* (Pittsburgh, 1941). There is a long, unwritten history of river improvement and navigational maintenance, much of it preserved in state and local archives and some in published records.

The steamboat saga constitutes one of the great romantic stories of American technology which has captured the imagination and found a place in the general histories. A satisfactory, semipopular account of this development is available in James Thomas Flexner, *Steamboats Come True: American Inventors in Action* (N. Y., 1944). The immediate recognition of the importance of the steamboat not only produced a vast literature of narrative and controversy, but it was also responsible for the preservation of many of the pertinent manuscripts of the leading steamboat figures. Among the key contemporary publications are: John Fitch, *The Original Steamboat Supported* (Phila., 1788); James Rumsey, *A Short Treatise on the Application of Steam* (Phila., 1788); and Oliver Evans, "On the Origin of Steam Boats and Steam Waggons" (1812), best consulted in the edition by Arlan K. Gilbert in *Delaware History*, 7 (1957), 142–67.

Of the large number of biographies of principals, the best technical study remains Henry W. Dickinson, *Robert Fulton, Engineer and Artist* (London, 1913). Good, too, is Archibald D. Turnbull, *John Stevens, an American Record* (N. Y., 1928), who used the manuscripts and offers several answers on technological questions. Greville Bathe, *An Engineer's Miscellany* (Phila., 1938), includes a good technical presentation of some of Fitch's work. Also related are Bathe's *Three Essays: A Dissertation on the Genesis of Mechanical Transport in*

America before 1800 (St. Augustine, Fla., 1960), *The Rise and Decline of the Paddle Wheel* (St. Augustine, Fla., 1962), and *Oliver Evans*.

So good that it emphasizes the inadequacies of everything else written on steamboats is Louis C. Hunter, *Steamboats on the Western Rivers* (Cambridge, Mass., 1949). This presents an excellent study of both engine and boat design and adaptation, demonstrating effectively the different patterns and evolution of the western boats from the eastern riverboats. Carl D. Lane's *American Paddle Steamboats* (N. Y., 1943), though larger in scope, is shorter and less analytical than Hunter's work but gives good information on design and specifications of boats and engines. Robert MacFarlane, *History of Propellers and Steam Navigation* (N. Y., 1851), is antique in style but draws from direct knowledge of the critical period. Marestier's *Memoir* (see page 51) offers similar insights plus a broader perspective.

6. *Canals.*—The canal era, achieved by a notable cooperation of groups and communities and celebrated in song and story, rested directly upon a technology which has been less studied than other aspects of the episode. There are no satisfying surveys but there are many histories of individual canals. Some of the best and most interested in physical elements were written by contemporaries: [William Smith], *An Historical Account of the Rise, Progress, and Present State of Canal Navigation in Pennsylvania* (Phila., 1795); Joshua Gilpin, *A Memoir on the Rise, Progress, and Present State of the Chesapeake and Delaware Canal* (Wilmington, 1821); and Elkanah Watson, *History of the Rise, Progress, and Existing Conditions of the Western Canals in the State of New-York* (Albany, 1820).

More fundamental are the very large number of reports and published documents relating to canals and canal construction: there are state canal commissioners' reports, engineers' reports, reports and statements of canal companies, laws, and proposals and retorts. One basic collection of this sort is *Laws of the State of New York, in Relation to the Erie and Champlain Canals, Together with the Annual Reports of the Canal Commissioners, and Other Documents*, 2 vols. (Albany, 1825). In general, the proposals and engineers' reports are most useful for technology. Christopher Colles, *Proposal of a Design for the Promotion of the Interests of the United States of America* (N. Y., 1808), suggested wooden canals built over the surface of the land with practically no excavation. Benjamin Henry Latrobe's most pertinent report is his *Letters to the Honourable Albert Gallatin . . . and Other Papers Relative to the Chesapeake and Delaware Canal* (Phila., 1808). Full of ideas is Robert Fulton, *A Treatise on the Improvement of Canal Navi-*

gation (London, 1796). [William Strickland], *Communication from the Chesapeake and Delaware Canal Company* (Phila., 1823), is an engineer's report, although heavily concerned with costs. An unusual series of trial runs is described in A. D. Bache, *Report of Experiments on the Navigation of the Chesapeake and Delaware Canal by Steam* (Phila., 1834).

Very well regarded but only slightly interested in the physical character of canals is the recent Carter Goodrich, Julius Rubin, H. Jerome Cranmer, and Harvey H. Segal, *Canals and American Economic Development* (N. Y., 1961). Julius Rubin, *Canal or Railroad? Imitation and Innovation in the Response to the Erie Canal in Philadelphia, Baltimore, and Boston,* in APS, *Transactions,* New Ser., 51 (1961), Pt. VII, grapples with responses in which technology was an element.

Many of the canals have had twentieth-century histories, either in book or article form. The greatest of the projects is chronicled in Noble E. Whitford, *History of the Canal System of the State of New York,* 2 vols. (Albany, 1906) and in a new study by Ronald E. Shaw, *Erie Water West* (Lexington, Ky., 1966). Other histories giving some attention to construction and physical characteristics are: Christopher Roberts, *The Middlesex Canal* (Cambridge, Mass., 1938); Walter S. Sanderlin, *The Great National Project: A History of the Chesapeake and Ohio Canal* (Baltimore, 1946); Wayland F. Dunaway, *History of the James River and Kanawha Company* (N. Y., 1922); and James William Putnam, *The Illinois and Michigan Canal* (Chicago, 1918). Unpublished accounts include William J. Reid, The Cape Cod Canal (Ph.D. diss., Boston U., 1958); Joseph H. Harrison, Jr., Internal Improvements and the American Union from Washington to Van Buren (Ph.D. diss., U. Va., 1954); and Harry N. Scheiber, Internal Improvements and Economic Change in Ohio, 1820–60 (Ph.D. diss., Cornell U., 1962).

7. *Railroads.*—Nothing so well typifies the American achievement in technology during the first half of the nineteenth century as the railroad. It embodied both the large-scale engineering involved in putting through the track and the best techniques of machine production in building engines, cars, and equipment. Many contemporaries regarded it as the symbol of the American spirit. It has awakened appropriate response in a very large literature of magazines, journals, and books. Enthusiasts are and have been legion; they collect and they publish. Among all the publication, there is some attention to technology; but most of this is in details. There are no satisfactory large surveys.

Most of the large railroad companies have official histories; some have had several variously motivated histories. They are often illustrated and offer at least guidance to the early technology of railroading. William Bender Wilson, *History of the Pennsylvania Railroad Company* (Phila., 1899), is by a civil engineer. Others are: Edward Hungerford, *The Story of the Baltimore and Ohio Railroad,* 2 vols. (N. Y., 1928); *A Century of Progress: History of the Delaware and Hudson Company* (Albany, 1925); and Samuel M. Derrick, *Centennial History of the South Carolina Railroad* (Columbia, 1930). Among regional studies, Thelma M. Kistler, *The Rise of Railroads in the Connecticut River Valley* (Northampton, 1938), is scholarly and economic; Alvin F. Harlow, *Steelways of New England* (N. Y., 1946), is more popular. Also popular is a general review with attention to physical aspects and early photographs by John W. Starr, Jr., *One Hundred Years of American Railroading* (N. Y., 1928).

Some early accounts and manuals are a source of more precise information. Because much of this material is elusive, an unusually good guide should be mentioned: Thomas R. Thomson, *Check List of Publications on American Railroads before 1841* (N. Y., 1942). Thomas Earle, *A Treatise on Rail-roads and Internal Communications* (Phila., 1830), and [John Stevens], *Documents tending to Prove the Superior Advantages of Rail-Ways and Steam Carriages over Canal Navigation* (N. Y., 1812), both seek to prove that railroads offer more than their competitors. S. W. Roberts, *An Account of Portage Rail Road, over the Allegheny Mountain in Pennsylvania* (Phila., 1836), describes an element of the transitional Pennsylvania system. Dionysius Lardner, *Railway Economy* (N. Y., 1850), is English but has a chapter on the United States and offers some helpful comparisons. Thomas Tredgold, *A Practical Treatise* (London, 1835), is the most used English manual. Two revealing American manuals are S. H. Long, *Rail Road Manual,* 2 vols. (Baltimore, 1828–29), and Simeon Borden, *A System of Useful Formulae* (Boston, 1851).

Other contemporary pieces urged the adoption of specific inventions. [Benjamin Henry Latrobe, Jr.], *Description of a new form of Edge Rail, to be called the Z rail* (n.p., [1840]), describes one of a large number of proposed rail forms. James Herron, *A Practical Description of Herron's Patent Trellis Railway Structure* (Phila., 1841), describes a new method of holding and supporting the track. George Escol Sellers, *Improvements in Locomotive Engines, and Railways* (Cincinnati, 1849), offers positive "adhesion wheels" to improve performance on steep grades. *Experiments on Rail Roads, in England* (Baltimore, 1829) was a part of Ross Winans' campaign to sell locomotives.

There are a very large number of engineers' reports, most of them applying to a single railroad or a single project. *Ensamples [sic] of Railway Making; which although not of English Practice are submitted with Practical Illustrations to the Civil Engineer, and the British and Irish Public* (London, 1843) is one of John Weale's glossy books which partakes of the nature of a survey of American practice; it is based on contributions by American engineers. Charles B. Stuart, *Report on the Tonawanda Rail Road* (N. Y., 1852), is an especially good technical report. Minor surveys are involved in Jonathan Knight and Benjamin H. Latrobe, [Jr.], *Report on the Plan of Construction of Several of the Principal Rail Roads in the Northern and Middle States* (Baltimore, 1838), as well as their *Report upon the Locomotive Engines, and the Police Management of Several of the Principal Rail Roads in the Northern and Middle States* (Baltimore, 1838).

Detailed studies of recent years approach the subject from several angles. There has been much interest in locomotives; a brief survey based largely on museum pieces and models is Smith Hempstone Oliver, *The First Quarter-century of Steam Locomotives in North America* (Washington, 1956). Angus Sinclair, *Development of the Locomotive Engineer* (N. Y., 1907), is also concerned with the engine. A recent study with rich appendices is John H. White, *Cincinnati Locomotive Builders, 1845–1868* (U. S. National Museum, *Bulletin*, No. 245 [Washington, 1965]). Two studies of track are L. R. Loree, "Track," *Bulletin of the University of Wisconsin, Engineering Series*, 1 (1894), 1–24, and J. Elfreth Watkins, "The Development of American Rail and Track," *U.S. National Museum Report, 1888–89* (Washington, 1889), 651–708. Biographies are many fewer than might be anticipated. One of the major figures has at least a minor biography: George L. Vose, *A Sketch of the Life and Works of George W. Whistler, Civil Engineer* (N. Y., 1887).

8. *Roads.*—Land travel constitutes a part of all surveys of American transportation, but it is the social aspects that have been most dramatized and developed; very few technological aspects have been brought into view. Although records relating to roads are plentiful in town, country, province, and state archives, they are very thin on technology.

One early survey is reasonably specific and has recently been equipped with a modern introduction: Christopher Colles, *A Survey of the Roads of the United States of America, 1789*, ed. by Walter W. Ristow (Cambridge, Mass., 1961). By mid-century, an excellent treatise on road construction had appeared; it is almost a better guide to what roads were not than to what they were, for the author comments that American roads were inferior to those of any other civilized country. This is W. M. Gillespie, A *Manual of the Principles and Practice of Road-Making* (3rd edn., N. Y., 1849). Less valuable is S. DeWitt Bloodgood, *A Treatise on Roads* (Albany, 1838). One of the strangest developments of the entire era, another index of the availability of lumber and the need for cheap construction, is chronicled in W. Kingsford, *History, Structure, and Statistics of Plank Roads, in the United States and Canada* (Phila., 1852).

Among recent writings, two works accord attention to the Conestoga wagon, one of the contributions of the colonial period: George Shumway, *et al.*, *Conestoga Wagon, 1750–1850* (York, Pa., 1964), and Don H. Berkebile, *Conestoga Wagons in Braddock's Campaign, 1755* (U.S. National Museum, *Bulletin*, No. 218 [Washington, 1959], pp. 142–53). Although brief, the latter work is concerned with the physical aspects of the wagon as well as with the historical episode.

Still the best survey of turnpikes is Joseph A. Durrenberger, *Turnpikes* (Valdasta, Tex., 1931). Robert F. Hunter, "Turnpike Construction in Antebellum Virginia," *Technology and Culture*, 4 (1963), 177–200, shows some of the possibilities in using state reports. More comprehensive but less specifically technical is Frederick J. Wood, *The Turnpikes of New England and Evolution of the Same* (Boston, 1919). W. Turrentine Jackson, *Wagon Roads West: A Study of Federal Road Surveys and Construction in the Trans-Mississippi West, 1846–1869* (Berkeley, 1952), is a good piece of work, although it barely overlaps the early American period.

9. *Bridges.*—Bridges were built from an early time in the colonial period, but they were not a necessity because cheaper substitutes were available in the form of fords and ferries. Key roads into the larger cities were sometimes equipped with bridges, if the span was not too difficult, but the large-scale construction of bridges and innovation in their design began with the demands of the railroads. The invention of new trusses became for a time a popular pastime, with the stimulus of large rewards for the successful.

Contemporary treatises on bridge building are all post-Revolutionary. Manuscripts on bridge design were submitted to the American Philosophical Society, but the first publication appears to have been Charles W. Peale, *An Essay on Building Wooden Bridges* (Phila., 1797), in which he proposes a patent bridge for the Schuylkill. Thomas Pope, *A Treatise on Bridge Architecture; in which the Superior Advantages of the Flying Pendent Lever Bridge are Fully Proved* (N. Y., 1811), presents a novel bridge form against a background of considerable study. In contrast to these bridges which were never built, A *Description of Ithiel Town's Improvement in the Construction of Wood and Iron Bridges* (New Haven, 1821) describes one of the most successful and most used of the patent trusses. The chief American contribution to the development of the principles of bridge building is Squire Whipple, *An Elementary and Practical Treatise on Bridge Building* (orig. edn., 1847, N. Y., 1873). Herman Haupt, *General Theory of Bridge Construction* (N. Y., 1851), is less inventive although based on experience as a Pennsylvania Railroad engineer, experiments, reading, and a search for principles. Still less original and more like an elementary textbook is a series of articles sometimes cut out and pasted together: Simeon S. Post, "Treatise on Principles of Civil Engineering as Applied to the Construction of Wooden Bridges," *American Railroad Journal*, 32 (1859), scattered pages between 226 and 423.

From a technical viewpoint perhaps the best review of bridge building is David B. Steinman and Sara Ruth Watson, *Bridges and Their Builders* (N. Y., 1941); a more detailed study which partly overlaps the early American period is David B. Steinman, *The Builders of the Bridge: The Story of John Roebling and His Son* (N. Y., 1945). A contemporary comparison of American and English bridges is offered in K. Culmann, "Der Bau der Eisernen Brücken in England und Amerika," *Allgemeine Bauzeitung mit Abbildung*, 17 (1852), 163–222. A recent review of American developments is Llewellyn N. Edwards, *A Record of History and Evolution of Early American Bridges* (Orono, Me., 1959). Eric Sloane, *American Barns and Covered Bridges* (N. Y., 1954), is the work of an enthusiast and, although without scholarly apparatus, has much valuable information. Carl W. Condit, *American Building Art: The Nineteenth Century* (N. Y., 1960), is as brilliant on bridges as on the more obvious emphases of his work.

10. *Building.*—Building was a basic and continuous technological activity even more universal than agriculture itself. Moreover, it was a composite of crafts and techniques; many of the elements of building appear in this bibliography under such headings as "Crafts and Craftsmen," "Tools, Woodwork," "Heat, Light," and "Engineers" (see pages 67–69, 83, 51–52). Whether by amateurs, carpenters, colonial master builders, or men who finally called themselves architects and engineers, building should be regarded as a part of the larger story of engineering. The construction aspects of architecture have been minimized by some

historians who are primarily interested in aesthetics. In fact, the union of architecture with several branches of engineering is well illustrated in the notable careers of Latrobe and Strickland in the nineteenth century.

In the colonial period, building skills were brought over by the men who practiced them; then and long afterward, they imported British manuals on carpentry and architecture. In time some were reprinted here, one of the first being Abraham Swan, A Collection of Designs in Architecture (Phila., 1775). Swan, who called himself a carpenter, offers not only house plans but bridge designs as well. Later works reissued in America were: Peter Nicholson, The Carpenter's New Guide (10th edn., Phila., 1830); Robert Meikleham, Dictionary of Architecture, 3 vols. (Phila., 1854); and George Wightwick, Hints to Young Architects (1st Amer. edn., N. Y., 1847).

The next step was the publication of American manuals. Owen Biddle, who called himself a "House Carpenter, and Teacher of Architecture," wrote The Young Carpenter's Assistant; or a System of Architecture Adapted to the Style of Building in the United States (Phila., 1805). More ambitious were the writings of A. J. Downing, such as his Cottage Residences (N. Y., 1844), and Benjamin Asher, who wrote in the 1840's and 1850's. Asher's works are most accessible in A Reprint of the Country Builder's Assistant, The American Builder's Companion, The Rudiments of Architecture, The Practical House Carpenter, The Practice of Architecture (N. Y., 1917).

The forthcoming guide to the A. Lawrence Kocher Collection of Colonial Williamsburg will provide an expanded list of such publications as those cited above as well as a guide to secondary literature. Meanwhile, some help is available in Alexander J. Wall, Books on Architecture Printed in America, 1775–1830 (N. Y., 1925), and in Charles B. Wood III, "A Survey and Bibliography of Writings on English and American Architectural Books Published Before 1895," Winterthur Portfolio, 2 (1965), 127–37.

More basic source materials exist in the preserved, restored, and recorded buildings of the early American period. These can be approached through well-known restorations and also, in several of the eastern cities, through commissions and offices recently established to preserve historic buildings and to record information about them. The National Park Service has similar information which it continues to collect at an expanded rate, but the largest concentration of data on buildings remains the Historic American Buildings Survey materials deposited in the Library of Congress. These archives are recorded in Catalog of the

Measured Drawings and Photographs of the Survey in the Library of Congress (Washington, 1941) and *Catalog Supplement* (Washington, 1959).

Detailed studies upon which the history of the technology of building must rest are not yet available in any depth. Many of the elements of building call for studies such as Robert W. Lesley, *History of the Portland Cement Industry in the United States* (N. Y., 1924). There are numbers of occasional articles which represent good beginnings, among them those of Charles E. Peterson, "Early American House-Warming by Coal Fires," Society of Architectural Historians, *Journal*, 9 (1950), 21–23; "Notes on Copper Roofing in America to 1802," *ibid.*, 24 (1965), 313–18; and "Early American Prefabrication," *Gazette de Beaux-Arts*, 6th Ser., 33 (1948), 37–46.

Among the voluminous writings of architectural historians, there is a great deal to be found upon the technology of building even though it is seldom the primary consideration. The works of Marcus Whiffen are distinguished by their attention to building and building techniques; of special note are: *The Public Buildings of Williamsburg: Colonial Capital of Virginia* (Williamsburg, 1958) and *The Eighteenth-Century Houses of Williamsburg: A Study of Architecture and Building in the Colonial Capital of Virginia* (Williamsburg, 1960). Surveys are less satisfying although there is helpful attention to building in Hugh Morrison, *Early American Architecture* (N. Y., 1952), and some attention to the early period in James M. Fitch, *American Building: The Forces that Shape It* (Boston, 1948). The forthcoming two volume edition of the latter work should be still more useful. Among the few biographies of colonial builder-architects are Rosamond Randall Beirne and John Henry Scarff, *William Buckland, 1734–1774: Architect of Virginia and Maryland* (Baltimore, 1958), and Carl Bridenbaugh, *Peter Harrison: First American Architect* (Chapel Hill, 1949).

Only recently has the technology of building been sufficiently isolated and examined in enough detail in Carl W. Condit, *American Building Art: The Nineteeth Century*. For the period he considers, his achievement is considerable, not only in confronting the processes and changes in methods of constructing buildings but also in studying bridges and dams.

11. *Other Engineering Works.*—The best large-scale American civil engineering surveys, such as those of Stevenson and Strickland, include notice of a variety of other works which have received very little individual attention. Among these are breakwaters, dams, piers, light-

houses, and water supply systems. Materials exist for the study of each of them, often in the form of local records and reports. The records of the federal government are more often accessible in published reports. This is true, for example, of the lighthouse system, one of the most helpful reports being *Light Houses: Report of the Secretary of the Treasury on the Improvements in the Light House System* (Washington, 1846).

Water supply and hydraulic engineering have attracted some attention. A onetime director of the Patent Office wrote a pioneer survey which includes American materials: Thomas Ewbank, *A Descriptive and Historical Account of Hydraulic and Other Machines* (N. Y., 1850). His treatment of American fire engines is especially good. Nelson M. Blake, *Water for the Cities: A History of the Urban Water-Supply Problem in the United States* (Syracuse, 1956), is not very technical but forms a good backdrop for placing contemporary accounts that are. There are many engineers' reports: *Report of William Weston, Esquire, on the Practicability of Introducing the Water of the River Bronx into the City of New York* ([N. Y.], 1799); B. Henry Latrobe, *A View of the Practicability and Means of Supplying the City of Philadelphia with Wholesome Water* (Phila., 1799); Nathan Hale, Jr., *Proceedings before a Joint Special Committee of the Massachusetts Legislature* (Boston, 1845). For a history of New York's efforts and successes, see Edward Wegmann, *The Water Supply of the City of New York, 1658–1895* (N. Y., 1896). One index of the magnitude of the problem of supplying water to all American cities is the appearance of a general textbook based largely on French treatises: Charles S. Storrow, *A Treatise on Water-Works for Conveying and Distributing Supplies of Water* (Boston, 1835).

G. Power

Non-human sources of energy in this period were pretty much limited to animal, wind, water, and steam. Considering the long and overwhelming dependence on horses, and the minor use of oxen, for agriculture and overland carriage, it is amazing that the subject has attracted only peripheral attention. Although horse mills and ox mills were long used for stationary power, very little can be found on them. Wind was the initial energy source utilized for all ocean crossings and for some lake and river carriage; in these forms, it has received attention. Stationary wind power in the form of windmills was important in some English areas as well as in those colonized by the Dutch, but the bibliography on American windmills is hardly comparable to that for British. With water power, more interest begins to be evinced—both in the water wheel and in the water turbine. This, however, is as nothing compared with the amount of writing poured out on steam power. The bulk of these publications is a proper measure of the magnitude of the steam engine's influence; it is not a fair gauge of its intrinsic importance. Much more work needs to be done on steam, but it is desirable that it not continue to obscure the other stories.

1. *Wind and Water.*—Wind and water mills have had an air of quaintness about them which attracts romantic attention; for example, see Marion Nicholl Rawson, *Little Old Mills* (N. Y., 1935), which goes on about wind, tide, and water mills. Fragmentary articles are more disciplined. A solid account concerned both with European and American windmills is F. H. Shelton, "Windmills, Picturesque and Historic: The Motors of the Past," *Journal of the Franklin Institute*, 187 (1919), 171–98. Too brief is Edward Pierce Hamilton, "Some Windmills of Cape Cod," Newcomen Society, *Transactions*, 5 (1925), 39–44.

For water power, some contemporary writings point in useful directions. John Nancarrow, "Calculations Relating to Grist and Saw Mills," APS, *Transactions*, 4 (1799), 348–61, weighs water power against steam power in these tasks. Perhaps the most significant publication is James B. Francis, *The Lowell Hydraulic Experiments* (N. Y., 1855), which followed his introduction of the Fourneyron turbine.

There are also good, technical articles on water power. Joseph R. Frizell, "The Old-Time Water-Wheels of America," American Society of Civil Engineers, *Transactions*, 28 (1893), 237–49, carefully describes the construction of the various elements. Charles T. Main, "Evolution of the Transmission of Water Power," in E. Everton Foster, *Lamb's Textile Industries* (Boston, 1916), I, 223–31, sketches the American improvements in Poncelet and Fourneyron turbines. Arthur T. Safford and Edward Pierce Hamilton, "The American Mixed-Flow Turbine and Its Setting," American Society of Civil Engineers, *Transactions*, 85 (1922), 1237–1356, gives the fullest account of the transition from the water wheel to the mixed-flow turbine. A major recent article is Louis C. Hunter, "Origines des Turbines Francis et Pelton," *Revue d'Histoire des Sciences*, 17 (1964), 209–42.

2. *Steam.*—The introduction and transition to steam power have been deservedly recognized as one of the fundamentally significant episodes in the history of technology—and, less frequently, as one of the most important episodes in American history. American contributions, adaptations, and uses of steam were great. As in most aspects of technology,

it is necessary to begin with the voluminous British writings on steam, which, especially in the surveys, are remarkably ready to fit in some notice of American work. Perhaps the most generally useful of many British histories is the recently reissued H. W. Dickinson, A Short History of the Steam Engine, with a new introduction by A. E. Musson (London, 1963). Of course, the general American histories give more attention to American elements of the story, from the early beginning of P. R. Hodge, The Steam Engine, Its Origin and Gradual Improvement from the Time of Hero to the Present Day (N. Y., 1840). The American survey with the most lasting influence has been Robert H. Thurston, A History of the Growth of the Steam Engine (orig. edn., 1878; Ithaca, 1939).

Of contemporary writings, those of Fitch and Rumsey on steamboats relate to steam engines and boilers, too, but the first big American contribution was Oliver Evans' Columbianum, or high-pressure steam engine. This he projected in his Abortion of the Young Steam Engineer's Guide (Phila., 1805), also published with a textual deletion as The Young Steam Engineer's Guide (Phila., 1805), and translated into French as Manuel de l'Ingénieur Mécanicien Constructeur de Machines à Vapeur (Paris, 1821). Partly in reaction against Evans' ideas, Benjamin Henry Latrobe published the pompously negative "First Report in Answer to the Enquiry Whether Any and What Improvements Have Been Made in the Construction of Steam Engines in America," APS, Transactions, 6 (1809), 89–98. Thomas Cooper put together a good synthetic account in "An Account of the Steam Engine," Emporium of Arts and Sciences, New Ser., 2 (1814), 1–220, 333–85.

Of the elements of the steam engine that have had special examination, perhaps the boiler is the most obvious. B. H. Bartol, A Treatise on the Marine Boilers of the United States (Phila., 1851), is not a treatise at all but a succession of important two-view drawings of specific boilers with data on operation and use. An uncritical biography is David Read, Nathan Read: His Invention of the Multi-Tubular Boiler and Portable High-Pressure Engine, and Discovery of the True Mode of Applying Steam-Power to Navigation and Railways (N. Y., 1870). A more reliable account of a water-tube boiler is Carl W. Mitman, "Stevens' Porcupine Boiler, 1804: A Recent Study," Newcomen Society, Transactions, 19 (1939), 165–71.

There are many other recent studies. Frederick Graff was separated by only a small gap of time from the Center Square, Philadelphia, engines he described in "Notice of the Earliest Steam Engines used in the United States," Journal of the Franklin Institute, 55 (1853), 269–71;

his drawings were used also in "The History of the Steam Engine in America," *ibid.*, 102 (1876), 253–68. Journalistic but serious is William Nelson, *Josiah Hornblower; and the First Steam Engine in America* (Newark, 1883). Here, too, the writings of Greville Bathe, previously mentioned, should be recalled. Most pertinent are *Oliver Evans* and, also written with Dorothy Bathe, *Jacob Perkins, His Inventions, His Times, and His Contemporaries* (Phila., 1943). Of some interest, too, is his *Citizen Genêt: Diplomat and Inventor* (Phila., 1946), inspired primarily by Genêt's work on steam-driven balloons.

One of the most promising pointers to future achievement in this field of history is Carroll W. Pursell, Jr., Stationary Steam Engines in America before the Civil War (Ph.D. diss., California, 1963, on Ann Arbor microfilm). It is a very sensitive story, in which the technical details are evaluated and put together with a historian's insight into their larger significance.

H. *Manufacturing*

No other term will suffice, but "manufacturing" is a particularly difficult word because during the early American period it had two different and, on the whole, opposite meanings. Initially it meant making things by hand, and at the end it meant making them by machine—in contrast to making them by hand. Further, "manufacturing" is sometimes used to distinguish a process of making relatively similar products —whether hand-blown bottles or pressed-glass plates—from designing and building a unique product—such as a church or a ship. In its various guises, manufacturing embraces a large part of the whole subject of technology, for most of technology is concerned with making things. Even when the object is transportation, communication, or measurement, it rests on made things. This section will embrace the making of all products—whether by hand or machine, whether unique or in multiples—unless placed under a previous heading.

1. *Crafts and Craftsmen.*—The colonial craftsman or artisan is often made to seem a different breed from the mechanic who built the nineteenth-century machines and the operative who tended them. This distinction was sometimes emphasized in Europe by conflict between the two classes, but in America the old craftsman often became the new mechanic—as did Oliver Evans and Chauncey Jerome. The distinction, in any case, has been exaggerated by the appropriation of the crafts and craftsmen by the collectors and art historians, who are primarily interested in the aesthetic values of the products, and by the concentra-

tion of historians of technology on the mechanics engaged in machine production. The craftsman and his work call for more attention in terms of technological history.

From this viewpoint, there are no surveys, but a useful panorama is offered in the "Williamsburg Craft Series" of pamphlets on many of the colonial trades. They are more broadly written than the Williamsburg focus suggests and their bibliographies are good. The titles so far published are: William De Matteo, *The Silversmith in Eighteenth-Century Williamsburg* (Williamsburg, 1956); Lloyd Payne, *The Miller in Eighteenth-Century Virginia* (Williamsburg, 1958); C. Clement Samford, *The Bookbinder in Eighteenth-Century Williamsburg* (Williamsburg, 1959); Johannes Heuvel, *The Cabinetmaker in Eighteenth-Century Williamsburg* (Williamsburg, 1958); August Klapper, *The Printer in Eighteenth-Century Williamsburg* (Williamsburg, 1964); Edward S. Tattershall, *The Wigmaker in Eighteenth-Century Williamsburg* (Williamsburg, 1959); and Herbert Clarke, *The Apothecary in Eighteenth-Century Williamsburg* (Williamsburg, 1965).

Comprehensive accounts of the crafts are available from a variety of backgrounds. An earlier work in the Institute's "Needs and Opportunities Series," Walter Muir Whitehill, *The Arts in Early American History*, gives the spirited account of an art historian, along with a valuable bibliography by Wendell and Jane Garrett. As a social historian, Carl Bridenbaugh, *The Colonial Craftsman* (N. Y., 1950), presents a penetrating picture of the broader role of the craftsman. Other works are more oriented toward the product. Erwin O. Christensen, *The Index of American Design* (N. Y., 1950), catalogs items from plows to furniture. Popular, limited, and of an antique shop flavor are: Scott Graham Williamson, *The American Craftsman* (N. Y., 1940) and Marion Nicholl Rawson, *Handwrought Ancestors* (N. Y., 1936). Edwin R. Tunis, *Colonial Craftsmen and the Beginnings of American Industry* (Cleveland, 1965), is profusely illustrated and often good.

A set of three works offers a combined index to the commercial productions of artisans as revealed in newspaper advertisements and notices. They are: George F. Dow, *The Arts and Crafts in New England, 1704–1775* (Topsfield, Mass., 1927); Rita S. Gottesman, *The Arts and Crafts in New York, 1726–1776; 1777–1799* (New-York Historical Society, *Collections*, 69, 81 [1938, 1954]); and Alfred C. Prime, *The Arts and Crafts in Philadelphia, Maryland, and South Carolina, 1721–1785; 1786–1800*, 2 vols. (Topsfield, Mass., 1929, 1932). In addition, the Winterthur Museum holds the Prime file of newspaper advertisements and a manuscript directory of Philadelphia craftsmen compiled from the city directories by Phoebe Phillips Prime. A still more localized study is Henry Wyckoff Belknap, *Trades and Tradesmen of Essex County, Massachusetts* (Salem, 1929).

Rolla Milton Tryon, *Household Manufactures in the United States, 1640–1860* (Chicago, 1917), represents the approach of an economic historian with a minor interest in technology. Colonial shop goods were, of course, handmade although later household products were often machine-made.

2. *Tools, Woodwork, Metalwork, and Machining.*—Surely one of the primary keys to the study of technology is knowledge of the tools which, in very considerable measure, define the character of the technology. The distance between plows or axes and reapers or milling machines marks a significant divide, but it does not separate unrelated categories. The most helpful work on hand tools is Henry C. Mercer, *Ancient Carpenters' Tools* (Doylestown, Pa., 1929). Because written in connection with the collections of the Bucks County Historical Society Museum, it retains greater importance for the American scene than the new W. L. Goodman, *The History of Woodworking Tools* (London, 1964). Also useful but brief is Frank H. Wildung, *Woodworking Tools at Shelburne Museum* (Shelburne, Vt., 1957). A graphic but thin general account is Eric Sloane, *A Museum of Early American Tools* (N. Y., 1964). Charles F. Hummel is preparing a monograph on the Dominy family of East Hampton, Long Island, clockmakers and cabinetmakers from 1757 to about 1840, whose woodworking shop has been reconstructed at the Winterthur Museum. He has already published an excellent illustrated article on "English Tools in America: The Evidence of the Dominys," *Winterthur Portfolio*, 2 (1965), 27–46.

Machine tools are usually conceived of in terms of metalwork, but of course they were applied effectively to wood and to other materials. Little of a separate nature has been written, but Richards, *Treatise on ... Woodworking Machines* is very helpful here too, despite its British origin (see page 44). Also applicable are the early volumes in John Jacob Holtzapffel, *Turning and Mechanical Manipulation*, 5 vols. (2nd edn., London, 1864–84).

When it comes to fine woodwork, there is little help except in the endless output of collectors' pieces. Insights of many sorts are offered in some of these; E. Milby Burton, *Charleston Furniture, 1700–1825* (Charleston, 1955), is one of the best. More in the folk tradition is Edward Deming and Faith Andrews, *Shaker Furniture: The Craftsmanship of an American Communal Sect* (New Haven, 1937). Some interest in manufacturing methods is shown in Mary Earle Gould, *Early American Wooden Ware and Other Kitchen Utensils* (Rutland, 1962).

M. V. Brewington, *Shipcarvers of North America* (Barre, Mass., 1962), is a different sort of work; although the focus is upon the figureheads themselves, the author's meticulous scholarship lifts the work to an unexpected value.

With machine tools proper, the beginning remains Joseph W. Roe, *English and American Tool Builders* (N. Y., 1916); Roe stands at the head of modern consideration of this whole subject. Among his other writings, the most pertinent are a series of articles on "Early American Mechanics," *American Machinist*, 41 (1914), 729–34, 903–8, 1077–82, and "Machine Tools in America," *Journal of the Franklin Institute*, 225 (1938), 499–511. A case study of the influence of an incredible Vermont center is unfolded, sometimes carelessly, in Guy Hubbard, "Development of Machine Tools in New England," *American Machinist*, 59–61 (1923–25), *passim*. L. T. C. Rolt, *A Short History of Machine Tools* (London, 1965), is an informed general survey.

An extension in depth of the work of Roe is found in the treatises of Robert S. Woodbury on the lathe, the gear-cutting, grinding, and milling machines. None of these is exclusively American, but the ones revealing the greatest American participation are *History of the Milling Machine* (Cambridge, Mass., 1960) and *History of the Grinding Machine* (Cambridge, Mass., 1959). This entire development is closely related to the rise of the American system of manufacturing by interchangeable parts (see pages 48–49).

Writings on the decorative metal arts usually come from the same craft-collectors' approach, and sometimes from the same authors, as works on cabinetmaking or pottery. The volume of such publications is very large. On silver, the best general survey is probably John Marshall Phillips, *American Silver* (N. Y., 1949). Craft-product approaches in other metals include: Ledlie Irwin Laughlin, *Pewter In America: Its Makers and Their Marks*, 2 vols. (Boston, 1940); Henry J. Kauffman, *Early American Copper, Tin, and Brass* (N. Y., 1950); Albert H. Sonn, *Early American Wrought Iron*, 3 vols. (N. Y., 1928); David McNeely Stauffer, *American Engravers on Copper and Steel* (N. Y., 1907); and an illustrated article on Britannia metal, Nancy A. Goyne, "Britannia in America: The Introduction of a New Alloy and a New Industry," *Winterthur Portfolio*, 2 (1965), 160–96. Of a different breed, although fine, antiquarian scholarship, is Lawrence C. Wroth, *Abel Buell of Connecticut: Silversmith, Type Founder and Engraver* (New Haven, 1926). This is an excellent little study of the range of technological activity in one man—Buell even constructed a cotton mill.

Economic historians have provided works which are on the whole more useful than those by collectors, especially in terms of the adoption of machine production. One of the best of these is George Sweet Gibb, *The Whitesmiths of Taunton: A History of Reed and Barton, 1824–1943* (Cambridge, Mass., 1943). Demonstrating an even larger proportionate interest in technology is Martha Van Hoosen Taber, *A History of the Cutlery Industry in the Connecticut Valley* (Northampton, 1955). Also excellent is the revealing study by Thomas R. Navin, *The Whitin Machine Works since 1831* (Cambridge, Mass., 1950). Yet, all of these writings are less pertinent than they would be if the authors' primary interest were in technology; the source materials are all excellent. For example, Elva Tooker, in *Nathan Trotter: Philadelphia Merchant, 1787–1853* (Cambridge, Mass., 1955), has used rich papers primarily to answer economic questions—"production" rather than the technology of sheet-metal manufacturing.

Older works are generally less scholarly. W. R. Wilbur, *History of the Bolt and Nut Industry of America* (Cleveland, 1905), is poorly organized. Still useful is Henry M. Smith, *Fifty Years of Wire Drawing* (Worcester, 1884). Most helpful on David Wilkinson and his screw-cutting machine is Israel Wilkinson's genealogically inspired *Memoirs of the Wilkinson Family in America* (Jacksonville, Ill., 1869).

In a class by itself as an index to the actual progress of a creative machinist is the *Early Engineering Reminiscences (1815–1840) of George Escol Sellers* (U.S. National Museum, *Bulletin*, No. 238 [Washington, 1965]), edited with imagination and a depth of insight by Eugene S. Ferguson. Other machine-shop reminiscences are presented in Robert Allison, "The Old and the New," American Society of Mechanical Engineers, *Transactions*, 16 (1895), 742–61.

3. *Clocks, Instruments, and the Technology of Science.*—The manufacture of clocks has been properly assigned a special place in the rise of machine technology. Early, in the handicraft period, a standard of measured precision and of machine production became a feature of clockmaking; it was not attained in other crafts until much later.

In this field, too, there is a large volume of collectors' guides, one of the most used being Brooks Palmer, *The Book of American Clocks* (N. Y., 1950). Of the same genre, yet more useful in specifics because of the author's practical knowledge, is George H. Eckhardt, *Pennsylvania Clocks and Clockmakers* (N. Y., 1955). The same author also has a more reined survey, *United States Clock and Watch Patents, 1790–1890* (N. Y., 1960). At a still higher level of accomplishment and brilliant in many of its insights is Penrose R. Hoopes, *Connecticut Clock-*

makers of the Eighteenth Century (Hartford and N. Y., 1930). He also offers an unusual, inside view of clockmaking as editor of *Shop Records of Daniel Burnap, Clockmaker* (Hartford, 1958). An American manual which also reveals some of the secrets of the trade is Thomas Reid, *A Treatise on Clock and Watch Making* (Phila., 1832). More valuable is the direct, opinionated, and vinegary *History of the American Clock Business for the Past Sixty Years, and Life of Chauncey Jerome, Written by Himself* (N. Y., 1860). The New York Public Library copy has been supplied with a typed index. This work gives some picture of the spread of interchangeable parts manufacture to clockmaking; the other actors in that drama are less well presented in print. Of some use, although anecdotal and written by a great-grandson, is John Ware Willard, *A History of Simon Willard, Inventor and Clockmaker* (New Haven, 1860). Brooke Hindle, *David Rittenhouse*, presents the leading eighteenth-century clockmaker who was even more celebrated as an instrument maker.

Instrument making was a trade often carried on in conjunction with clockmaking, and it was also closely related to the development of machine technology and the advance of technology through precision production. The first and most essential instruments were those related to surveying and navigation, and because of the fundamental importance of transportation in the advance of technology in the United States, these instruments retained their primacy when calipers, micrometers, gauges, and pyrometers rose to a new importance beside them.

The background is best sketched in Maurice Daumas, *Les Instruments Scientifiques aux XVIIe et XVIIIe Siècles* (Paris, 1953). There are no American manuals; several British manuals were used but the one that served Americans longest was probably Edmund Stone's translation of Nicholas Bion's treatise which went under the title of *The Construction and Principal Uses of Mathematical Instruments* (London, 1723). Several specific instruments developed in America are separately described. Thomas Godfrey's quadrant is presented by James Logan in the *Philosophical Transactions*, 38 (1734), 441–50; 39 (1736), 404–5. Later examples are: [Benjamin Dearborn], *The Patent Balance Compared with other Instruments for Weighing* (Phila., 1803); Benjamin Workman, *Gauging Epitomized* (Phila., 1788); and [George Wall, Jr.], *Description with Instructions for the Use of Wall's Newly Invented Surveying Instrument, called the Trigonometer* (Phila., 1788). Most erudite is James Cutbush, *Hydrostatics* (Phila., 1812), a treatise on hydrometers, primarily European.

A series of recent studies of instruments highlights a rising recognition of the importance of the field. Earliest, on Harvard College instruments, many of which were used as teaching devices, is I. Bernard Cohen, *Some Early Tools of Science* (Cambridge, Mass., 1950). Also more related to the dissemination of science than to technology are Robert P. Multhauf, comp., *A Catalogue of Instruments and Models in the Possession of the American Philosophical Society* (Phila., 1961), and Howard C. Rice, Jr., *The Rittenhouse Orrery* (Princeton, 1954). On surveying instruments, a collector and instrument manufacturer has produced an unorganized but useful compilation: Charles E. Smart, *The Makers of Surveying Instruments in America since 1700* (Troy, 1962). Better organized but still a compound of information obtained at varying depths is Silvio A. Bedini, *Early American Scientific Instruments and Their Makers* (U.S. National Museum, *Bulletin*, No. 231 [Washington, 1964]). Presenting excellent scholarship and illustrations is M. V. Brewington, *The Peabody Museum Collection of Navigating Instruments with Notes on Their Makers* (Salem, 1963).

The technology of science is a very large field, intricately bound with the advance of science itself, and a field which grew markedly through the early American period. The manufacture of instruments used in scientific study represents only one aspect, although a large aspect, of the technology of science; the general relationship of instruments to science is indicated in the preceding titles. In addition, there are other scientific instruments of less value to the advance of technology; most important is probably the telescope. One of the few pieces on early telescope manufacture is Robert P. Multhauf, Amasa Holcomb, Julia Fitz Howell, F. W. Preston, and William J. McGrath, Jr., *Holcomb, Fitz, and Peate: Three 19th Century American Telescope Makers* (U. S. National Museum, *Bulletin*, No. 228 [Washington, 1962], pp. 156–84). Robert Hare, *Strictures on a Publication Entitled Clark's Gas Blowpipe* (Phila., 1820), is a reflection of one American invention, very widely used in science. A collection of reprints put out by the American Pharmaceutical Association is George B. Griffinhagen, *Tools of the Apothecary* (Washington, 1957). As the scattered character of these references suggests, the field of the technology of science has hardly been defined, let alone surveyed.

4. *Glass and Pottery.*—Glassmaking preserved its secret, guild character longer than many other crafts, perhaps because of the high component of skill required. Throughout this period, skilled craftsmen

continued to be imported from Europe to supply the need, and no manuals comparable to those found in carpentry and shipbuilding exist to outline the details of the manufacturing process.

The best general approaches are provided by the collectors of surviving products. Rhea Mansfield Knittle, *Early American Glass* (N. Y., 1927), comes down in time little further than 1860 and deals carefully with techniques and changes in technique. More general and encyclopedic is George S. and Helen McKearin, *American Glass* (N. Y., 1941, 1948). Lura Woodside Watkins, *American Glass and Glassmaking* (N. Y., 1950), presents the history of the known glasshouses, while just one is detailed in Ruth Webb Lee, *Sandwich Glass: The History of the Boston and Sandwich Glass Company* (Framingham Centre, Mass., 1939). Albert Christian Revi, *American Pressed Glass and Figure Bottles* (N. Y., 1964), deals comprehensively with the results of a significant, and debated, technological change.

Many of the other works are of scattered character and direction. Aside from collectors' compilations, there is little on the important work of Stiegel, except for feeble reeds such as George L. Heiges, *Henry William Stiegel and His Associates: A Story of Early American Industry* ([Lancaster], 1948). Amelung is described in Dorothy Mackay Quynn, "Johann Friedrich Amelung at New Bremen," *Maryland Historical Magazine*, 43 (1948), 155–79. J. C. Harrington, *Glassmaking at Jamestown* (Richmond, 1952), is popular and brief but concerned first with technology. Bangs Burgess, *History of Sandwich Glass* (Yarmouthport, Mass., 1925), offers some conversations with old workers which convey a sense of the technology. The pamphlet by Kenneth M. Wilson, *Glass in New England* (Sturbridge, Mass., 1959), also focuses on processes. From the view of economic history is Warren G. Scoville, "Growth of the American Glass Industry to 1880," *Journal of Political Economy*, 52 (1944), 192–216. Specialized articles appear in the *Journal of Glass Studies*, an annual journal sponsored by the Corning Museum of Glass; each issue features a check-list of recently published articles and books on the art and history of glass making.

American pottery making is less satisfactorily handled, but, again, there is a large variety of collectors' publications. Based partly on excavations is Lura Woodside Watkins, *Early New England Potters and Their Wares* (Cambridge, Mass., 1950). John Spargo, *The Potters and Potteries of Bennington* (Boston, 1926), is a detailed story of a small area. Although not intended as a study of pottery, the best related archaeological report is strongest on pottery: Ivor Noël Hume, *Excavations at*

Rosewell in Gloucester County, Virginia, 1957–1959 (U. S. National Museum, *Bulletin*, No. 225 [Washington, 1962], 153–229). Mr. Hume also excavated the Amelung glass house in Baltimore and has publications in press of still greater importance to technology.

5. *Paper and Printing.*—Although the collecting impulse does not support the study of papermaking, it has received considerable attention from book collectors, paper companies, and historians. There are no early manuals on papermaking, but some help on early processes is offered in Charles Thomas Davis, *The Manufacture of Paper* (Phila. and London, 1886). The leading author in this field is Dard Hunter; his most pertinent work is *Papermaking in Pioneer America* (Phila., 1952). Behind this stands his comprehensive *Papermaking: The History and Technique of an Ancient Craft* (N. Y., 1943); both display fundamental concern for technology but are most successful with hand production. Although nothing but a list, Joel Munsell, *A Chronology of Paper and Paper-Making* (Albany, 1857), notes the major technological advances. Hardly more satisfying is Lyman Horace Weeks, *A History of Paper-Manufacturing in the United States, 1690–1916* (N. Y., 1916). Episodes in the development of papermaking in Delaware have recently been carefully studied in Harold B. Hancock and Norman B. Wilkinson, "The Gilpins and Their Endless Paper Machine," *Pennsylvania Magazine of History and Biography*, 81 (1957), 391–405, and Joseph W. Maxson, Jr., "Nathan Sellers, America's First Large Scale Maker of Paper Moulds," *The Paper Maker*, 29 (1960), 1–16.

Because the product of printing is the very substance of most historical scholarship, all bibliographies and published materials are in some measure comprehended within this heading. Even of bibliographies and histories of printing, there is a very long list. Most of them do not offer direct access to the technology, but there are manuals which do. British manuals were available to Americans, beginning with Moxon's in 1683: *Mechanick Exercises or the Doctrine of Handy-works Applied to the Art of Printing*, 2 vols. (N. Y., 1896). A better reflection of later practice is Thomas F. Adams, *Typographia: A Brief Sketch of the Origin, Rise, and Progress of the Typographic Art; with Practical Directions for Conducting Every Department in an Office* (Phila., 1837). Special attention is accorded to inventions, implements, and processes in J. Luther Ringwalt, *American Encyclopaedia of Printing* (Phila., 1871).

Although not primarily directed toward technology, the work of one leading printer is especially pertinent: Isaiah Thomas, *History of Print-*

ing in America, 2 vols. (Worcester, 1810). Lawrence C. Wroth has written frequently on printing and is probably most concerned with technology in *The Colonial Printer* (2nd edn., Portland, Me., 1938; paperback reprint, Charlottesville, 1965). One very important American advance is described in Jacob Kainen, *George Clymer and the Columbian Press* (San Francisco, 1950). In the same field is Robert Hoe and Co., *Short History of the Printing Press* (n.p., 1902), a pictorial review of the major presses. A key element of printing is studied in Rollo G. Silver, *Typefounding in America, 1787–1825* (Charlottesville, 1965).

American bookbinding has been neglected by collectors and historians alike. Hannah D. French contributed an introduction to "Early American Bookbinding by Hand" in Helmut Lehmann-Haupt, ed., *Bookbinding in America* (Portland, Me., 1941). A detailed report by members of Colonial Williamsburg's research staff is currently scheduled for publication: C. Clement Samford and John M. Hemphill II, *Bookbinding in Colonial Virginia* (Charlottesville, 1966).

6. *Leather.*—One of the most ancient crafts, leather tanning and working was a part of the American scene from almost the beginning. Technologically, the two phases of this industry followed different courses as Peter C. Welsh demonstrates in "A Craft That Resisted Change: American Tanning Practices to 1850," *Technology and Culture*, 4 (1963), 299–317, and *Tanning in the United States to 1850: A Brief History* (U.S. National Museum, *Bulletin*, No. 242 [Washington, 1964]). Tanning practices did not change markedly, but methods of manufacturing shoes were rapidly mechanized toward the end of the period. This latter story has been outlined in Blanche E. Hazard, *The Organization of the Boot and Shoe Industry in Massachusetts before 1875* (Cambridge, Mass., 1875), and Charles H. McDermott, ed., *A History of the Shoe and Leather Industries of the United States* (Boston, 1918).

There were no separate early manuals, and when Campbell Morfit tried to put one together at mid-century, he drew directly upon French writings: *The Arts of Tanning, Currying, and Leather Dressing ... from the French of Julia de Fontenelle and F. Malpyre* (Phila., 1852). A special plea for a patent process is the basis of David Kennedy, *The Art of Tanning Leather* (N. Y., 1857). A backward-looking review of a sort is offered in the ponderous Charles Thomas Davis, *The Manufacture of Leather ... To Which are Added Complete Lists of all American Patents for Materials, Processes, Tools, and Machines for Tanning, Currying, etc.* (Phila., 1885).

7. *Textiles.*—Textile manufacturing occupies an even more central position in the development of American technology than it does in English history. From the early—and continuing—use of spinning wheels and hand looms to the highly mechanized and coordinated production of the mid-nineteenth century, textiles were important in the American scene. Even during the colonial period the Americans succeeded in supplying their own fundamental clothing and textile needs. In constructing the textile mills, Americans developed much of the machine-shop technique required to extend mechanization to other fields. The linkage ran outward from textile centers to steam engines and railroads.

In the textile field the product collectors have produced some publications, but fortunately there is so much more that is directly concerned with technology that little dependence need be placed upon them. Several little museum pieces begin with the fabrics: Catherine Fennelly, *Textiles in New England, 1790–1840* (Sturbridge, Mass., 1961); Virginia D. Parslow, *Weaving and Dyeing Processes in Early New York* (Cooperstown, 1949); and Nancy Andrews Reath, *The Weaves of Hand-Loom Fabrics* (Phila., 1927). The fact that such writings need hardly be considered in seeking a view of textile technology only serves to emphasize the lack of better materials in many fields of manufacturing.

There are a few comprehensive surveys of the production of all textiles. Early enough to be almost dominated by technological interest is William R. Bagnall, *The Textile Industries of the United States Including Sketches and Notices of Cotton, Woolen, Silk, and Linen Manufactures in the Colonial Period*, Vol. I (Cambridge, Mass., 1893). Brief and unoriginal is Perry Walton, *The Story of Textiles* (Boston, 1925). E. Everton Foster, *Lamb's Textile Industries of the United States*, Vol. I (Boston, 1916), is uneven but some of the signed chapters are good.

Cotton textiles became the most important aspect of textile manufacturing in early America, most important quantitatively following the spread of the saw-tooth cotton gin and most important in terms of the advance of machine production. An excellent study which integrates technological elements is Caroline F. Ware, *The Early New England Cotton Manufacture* (Boston and N. Y., 1931). Melvin T. Copeland, *The Cotton Manufacturing Industry of the U.S.* (Cambridge, Mass., 1912), is more heavily economic. Written from the viewpoint of the mechanic is Samuel Webber, "Historical Sketch of the Commencement and Progress of the Cotton Manufacture in the

United States up to 1876," *Manual of Power* (N. Y., 1879). Samuel Slater's contribution has been recognized from an early point, but the best presentation probably remains George S. White, *Memoir of Samuel Slater* (2nd edn., Phila., 1836).

Fortunately, several of the major figures in the development of textile machine production understood their own historical role and left self-conscious records. The best survey by a participant is [Samuel Batchelder], *Introduction and Early Progress of the Cotton Manufacture in the United States* (Boston, 1863). Nathan Appleton, *Introduction of the Power Loom, and Origin of Lowell* (Lowell, 1858), is the account of a businessman who had an excellent knowledge of the machinery behind the achievements. Of some help, too, is the preliminary dispute, *Correspondence between Nathan Appleton and John A. Lowell in Relation to the Early History of the City of Lowell* (Boston, 1848). All of these publications are more valuable for their critical evaluations than for the simple details of machinery.

Of rare and special importance is the work of James Montgomery, Scottish cotton manufacturing expert who served for a time as superintendent of the York Factories in Saco, Maine. He first became known for his manual, *The Theory and Practice of Cotton Spinning; or the Carding and Spinning Master's Assistant* (2nd edn., Glasgow, 1833); but much more important for American history is his *A Practical Detail of the Cotton Manufacture of the United States of America and the State of the Cotton Manufacture of that Country Contrasted and Compared with that of Great Britain* (Glasgow, 1840). The significance of the latter work was extended by the controversies it aroused and the checks thereby established upon Montgomery's evaluations. The most accessible part of this is in Justitia, *Strictures on Montgomery on the Cotton Manufactures of Great Britain and America* (Newburyport, 1841).

Two other nineteenth-century commentaries demonstrate a strong historical sense. Evan Leigh, *The Science of Modern Cotton Spinning*, 2 vols. (2nd edn., Manchester, 1873), is good in its evaluation of American improvements. Robert H. Baird, *The American Cotton Spinner, and Managers' and Carders' Guide* (Phila., 1887), is a work put together in its entirety after the author's death.

Some more recent works are excellent on machinery and machine work. Especially outstanding from an economic-business history approach but keenly concerned with technology is George Sweet Gibb, *The Saco-Lowell Shops: Textile Machinery Building in New England, 1813–1949* (Cambridge, Mass., 1950). Of much the same caliber, although not reaching back so far in time, is Navin, *The Whitin Ma-*

chine Works. More specific and limited is Henry Stedman Nourse, "Some Notes on the Genesis of the Power Loom in Worcester County," *American Antiquarian Society, Proceedings,* 16 (1904), 22–46. Almost as brief and less inspired are: John L. Hayes, *American Textile Machinery* (Cambridge, 1879), and William H. Chase, *Five Generations of Loom Builders* (Hopedale, Mass., 1950).

Justifiably, woolen textile manufacturing has received much less attention than cotton, but the best survey in either field is Arthur Harrison Cole, *The American Wool Manufacture,* 2 vols. (Cambridge, Mass., 1926); it is economic history with a keen sense of the technology. A comparable work on carpet manufacturing is Arthur H. Cole and Harold F. Williamson, *The American Carpet Manufacture* (Cambridge, Mass., 1941). These works supersede earlier surveys, but a detail of the latter story is well presented in *Correspondence Relating to the Invention of the Jacquard Brussels Carpet Power Loom* (Boston, 1868). Good on the hardware is Grace L. Rogers, *The Scholfield Wool-Carding Machines* (U. S. National Museum, *Bulletin,* No. 218 [Washington, 1959], pp. 1–14).

Still less has been written on silk manufacturing, and the surveys that exist relate to the raising of silkworms as much as to manufacturing the cloth. A contemporary approach, really an argument in favor of the industry, is John d'Homergue and Peter Stephen Duponceau, *Essays on American Silk* (Phila., 1830). A later review is L. P. Brockett, *The Silk Culture in America* (N. Y., 1876).

8. *Chemicals.*—The manufacturing of chemicals falls into a subtly different category from mechanical technology. Colonial craftsmen made clocks and ships with little direct reference to books, to science, or to Europe, and mechanics in the republican period introduced innovations in spinning machinery and railroads that blazed paths across the world. With chemical manufactures, however, the dependence upon Europe was more obvious and more extended. In one branch or another, European skill had to be imported throughout the period, and more manuals proportionately were translated and reprinted in the United States.

This was a time of rapid advance in chemical knowledge and of a closer relationship between science and practice than in many other fields of production. This background, with a social history twist, is presented in Archibald and Nan L. Clow, *The Chemical Revolution: A Contribution to Social Technology* (London, 1952). A partially applicable comparison in terms of major industrial chemicals is discussed in L. F. Haber, *The Chemical Industry during the Nineteenth Century:*

A *Study of the Economic Aspects of Applied Chemistry in Europe and North America* (London, 1958). A very brief and thin coverage of this part of the American story is given in Williams Haynes, *American Chemical Industry*, Vol. I (N. Y., 1954).

The colonists quickly established a number of chemical industries; soap, salt, dyes, and bleaches remained important. The clearest literate record is left for potash because of the extensive parliamentary and private efforts to encourage its production. The best manuals, often reprinted, came from England; for example, Thomas Stephens, *The Method and Plain Process for making Pot-Ash* (London, [1755]). The best analyses and evaluations of American efforts also came from England: [Thomas Stephens], *The Rise and Fall of Pot-Ash in America* (London, 1758); [Robert] Dossie, *Observations on the Pot-Ash brought from America* (London, 1767); and W. Lewis, *Experiments and Observations on American Potashes* (London, 1767).

The Revolution stimulated development of several chemical industries, salt being the most simple in terms of process. This is briefly surveyed in Harry B. and Grace M. Weiss, *The Revolutionary Saltworks of the New Jersey Coast: With Notes on the Early Methods of Making Salt in New England, New York, Delaware, and Virginia* (Trenton, 1959). The reopening of old sources did not inhibit the advocacy of new processes for domestic production, as in James Fennell, *Description of the Principles and Plan of Proposed Establishments of Salt Works* (Phila., 1798).

Many chemical processes in widest use were commonly well understood but at the same time susceptible to much improvement. Manuals on distilling were very conscious of patents and new methods at the same time that they answered a widespread need for fundamentals. Two examples are: Michael Krafft, *The American Distiller; or the Theory and Practice of Distilling* (Phila., 1804), and Harrison Hall, *Hall's Distiller* (Phila., 1813).

Lead and paint production were rapidly growing fields. The best study here is based on extensive business papers, and shows concern for manufacturing processes: Miriam Hussey, *From Merchants to "Colour Men": Five Generations of Samuel Wetherill's White Lead Business* (Phila., 1956). Manuals in this field were few; one produced at mid-century, at a relatively low level, is *The Painter, Gilder, and Varnisher's Companion containing Rules and Regulations in Everything Relating to the Arts of Painting, Gilding, Varnishing, and Glass-Staining* (Phila., 1850).

Bleaching and dyeing depended much upon European treatises and innovations. James Haigh, *The Dier's Assistant* (Poughkeepsie, 1813), although published in the United States, is an Englishman's translation of French works plus his own observations. An unacknowledged translation of Berthollet constitutes much of the substance of Thomas Cooper, *A Practical Treatise on Dyeing, and Callicoe Printing; Exhibiting the Processes in the French, German, English, and American Practice of Fixing Colours on Woolen, Cotton, Silk and Linen* (Phila., 1815). Under the same title, *A Practical Treatise on Dyeing and Calico-Printing* (N. Y., 1846) is a much more sophisticated guide, with more American experience behind the author, "an Experienced Dyer. Assisted by Several Scientific Gentlemen." *The Dyer and Colour Maker's Companion* (Phila., 1850) is feebler but ostensibly American, too. Of limited use is the survey by Albert H. Heusser, *The History of the Silk Dyeing Industry in the United States* (Paterson, 1927). One of few recent efforts to put ample materials in order is Sidney M. Edelstein, "Origins of Chlorine Bleaching in America," *American Dyestuff Reporter*, 49 (1960), 254–63.

By the mid-nineteenth century, there were efforts both to apply chemistry to one field after another and to cover the whole in one treatise. Campbell Morfit, who also wrote on the application of chemistry to tanning, offered *Chemistry Applied to the Manufacture of Soap and Candles* (Phila., 1847) and *Perfumery: Its Manufacture and Use* (Phila., 1853). He described himself as a "practical and analytical chemist." One comprehensive manual is James Pilkington, *The Artist's Guide and Mechanic's Own Book, Embracing the Portion of Chemistry Applicable to the Mechanic Arts* (N. Y., 1841).

The manufacture of gunpowder and explosives is one of the chemical industries unfortunately marked by negative overtones, despite its central importance in military and civil engineering and its ramifications in many sectors of technology. A satisfactory general survey is available in Arthur P. Van Gelder and Hugo Schlatter, *History of the Explosives Industry in America* (N. Y., 1927). The impetus of the American Revolution was not sufficient to establish this industry, although it had some effects and left some recipe books and manuals: for example, *The Process for Extracting and Refining Salt-Petre* (Phila., 1774), and *New York Essays upon the Making of Salt-petre and Gunpowder* (N. Y., 1776).

The effective establishment and growth of the industry depended much upon Europe; E. I. du Pont not only brought his own knowledge but continued to rely on Bottée and Riffault, *Traité de l'Art de Fabriquer la Poudre à Canon* (Paris, 1811). One specific published piece of some value is E. I. du Pont's own "On the Manufacture of War and Sporting Powder in the United States," in B. G. du Pont, *E. I. du Pont de Nemours and Company, 1802–1902* (Boston and N. Y., 1920). Some of the information available in the corpus of the Du Pont papers held by the Eleutherian Mills-Hagley Foundation has been pulled out in research reports, exhibits, and more general writings, especially by Norman B. Wilkinson.

Drugs had a British beginning in the colonial period, but in the nineteenth century most of the foundations of drug and fine chemical production were laid by men with Continental training. A general survey on a company-by-company basis is available in Glenn Sonnedecker, *Kremers and Urdangs History of Pharmacy* (3rd edn., Phila., 1963).

9. *Other Manufacturing.*—Many fields of manufacturing are not included in the foregoing discussion. Some are minor stories with very little in print about them. An example of this is [Perry Walton], *Comb Making in America* (Boston, 1925); although not a model study, it does present the transition from hand to machine production. Other manufactures made only their initial appearance in this period, their fulfillment lying in the next. This is the case of the applications of vulcanized rubber following Charles Goodyear's discovery of 1839, and of the production of sewing machines following Elias Howe's patent of 1846. These developments suffer further from generally inadequate studies.

One type of manufactures sharing several of the characteristics of the preceding categories is coin and bank-note production. This field enjoys the participation of a well-disciplined group of collectors; American Numismatic Society publications are usually of scholarly caliber. Such, for example, are Sydney P. Noe, *The Oak Tree Coinage of Massachusetts* (N. Y., 1947) and *The New England Willow Tree Coinages of Massachusetts* (N. Y., 1943). From the same background comes a good survey of paper money, George L. McKay, *Early American Currency* (N. Y., 1944). Interested in the machinery and processes of coinage rather than the product is Frank H. Stewart, *History of the First United States Mint* (n.p., 1924). One of the American advances in bank-note engraving was made by Jacob Perkins before his emigration, and is described in his *The Permanent Stereotype Steel Plate* (Newburyport, Mass., 1806). The Bathes' biography of Jacob Perkins is helpful here too.

I. *Heat, Light, and Electricity*

These fields did not emerge as separate engineering categories in early America, but there was from the beginning much activity in supplying heating and lighting needs, and it deserves historical attention. Many manufacturing processes required heat, and its production is a side story in some of the treatises noted above. Space heating attracted a curious concentration of interest on the part of Americans, from the writings of Franklin and Rumford to the large-scale production of stoves of various sorts at mid-century. Most familiar of the American writings are Benjamin Franklin's *An Account of the New Invented Pennsylvania Fire-Places* (Phila., 1744) and "On the Cause and Cure of Smoky Chimneys," APS, *Transactions*, 2 (1786), 1–36. American contributions are well noted even in the English account, *The Theory and Practice of Warming and Ventilating Public Buildings, Dwelling-houses, and Conservatories* (London, 1825). One inquiry in America, announced as scientific in character and practical in objective, provoked much controversy: Marcus Bull, *Experiments to Determine the Comparative Value of the Principal Varieties of Fuel* (Phila., 1827). More satisfying is a better limited and controlled inquiry: Walter R. Johnson, *Report of the Navy Department . . . on American Coals, Applicable to Steam Navigation* (Washington, 1849).

Cooling was restricted largely to food processing and came, except in such unstudied examples as the spring house, relatively late. Richard O. Cummings, *The American Ice Harvests: A Historical Study in Technology, 1800–1918* (Berkeley and Los Angeles, 1949), offers thin coverage of this important story.

Lighting technology is a part of many episodes: of candles made in the home, shop, and factory; of whale oil lamps; of tinsmith's lanterns; and of gas lamps. A collector's approach to one aspect of the story is found in Arthur H. Hayward, *Colonial Lighting* (Boston, 1923). The production and use of coal gas comes into the reports of such engineers as Strickland. Guidance drawn from British practice in the use of gas for lighting is utilized in Thomas Cooper, *Some Information Concerning Gas Lights* (Phila., 1816).

Electricity was not a technological matter until the nineteenth century, except for occasional medical fads and for static studies. A good guide, which does not attempt total coverage, is Harold I. Sharlin, *The Making of the Electrical Age: From the Telegraph to Automation* (N. Y., 1963). In fact, the telegraph represents the major episode of the early American era in electrical development, and it is served by a long list of writings. A biographical approach is Carleton Mabee, *The American Leonardo: A Life of Samuel F. B. Morse* (N. Y., 1943). Of the surveys, an early account which displays some interest in the technology is Alexander Jones, *Historical Sketch of the Electric Telegraph* (N. Y., 1852). A scholarly, recent review is Robert L. Thompson, *Wiring a*

Continent (1832–1866) (Princeton, 1947). A surprisingly early industrial use of electricity is sketched in the American edition of an English manual, Charles V. Walker, *Electrotype Manipulation* (Phila., 1844). The use of electricity for power had only the barest beginnings; one such start is a part of Clark C. Spence's article, "Early Use of Electricity in American Agriculture," *Technology and Culture*, 3 (1962), 142–60.

J. Education, Organization, and Science

The formal surveys of technical education focus on the late engineering schools: for example, Charles Riborg Mann, A *Study of Engineering Education* (N. Y., 1918). They are especially unsatisfying because they come to grips with such a very small part of the full picture. Craft apprenticeships were the rule in the colonial period, and traditional education had little relevance to technology. Some help with this early pattern is given in Marcus W. Jernegan, *Laboring and Dependent Classes in Colonial America, 1607–1783* (Chicago, 1931), and Bridenbaugh, *Colonial Craftsman*. Bernard Bailyn, *Education in the Forming of American Society: Needs and Opportunities for Study* (Chapel Hill, 1960), presents a strong plea for studying education in terms of all the elements of society which participated in transmitting the heritage, not the schools alone. So far as technology is concerned, this study has not begun.

The manual or handbook was one of the important means of transmitting technology and techniques from the skilled to the uninformed. How-to-do-it books were popular throughout the colonial period in medicine and law and in technology. Even a skilled cabinetmaker or carpenter needed guidance beyond the limits of his memory when he tried to produce a variety of goods in the fashion of the mother country. Initially, these manuals were generally of British origin; increasingly at the time of the Revolution they were reprinted in America; then they were recast, written anew, or translated from French and German originals. This literature is too large to examine here, but specimens have been introduced into many of the sections above. In England, E. and F. N. Spon and John Weale were publishers especially active in supplying technical manuals. One useful guide is *Weale's Catalogue of Works Recently Published on the Various Branches of Civil and Military Engineering, Architecture, Mechanics, Naval Architecture and Steam Navigation* (London, 1848). In the United States, probably as active as any were H. C. Carey and I. Lea of Philadelphia and Charles B. Norton of New York.

One manual reprinted by Carey and Lea is outstanding because of the significance of the American additions to their edition: John Nicholson, *The Operative Mechanic and British Machinist; being a Practical Display of the Manufactories and Mechanical Arts of the United Kingdom*, 2 vols. (Phila., 1826). Similarly, the edition by "an American Physician" of another British book, [Colin] *MacKenzie's Five Thousand Receipts in all the Useful and Domestic Arts* (Phila., 1846), is valuable for its additions. No doubt many of the reprints have such utility, but they have to be read closely to ascertain the additions.

Toward mid-century the better manuals of American origin tended away from a cookbook form and toward a reliance on principles and theory, paralleling the direction of institutional education. Examples include Leonard Charles Eldredge, *The Mechanical Principia; Containing all the Various Calculations on Water and Steam Power and on the Different Kinds of Machinery Used in Manufacturing* (N. Y., 1848), and Frederick Overman, *Mechanics for the Millwright, Machinist, Engineer, Civil Engineer, Architect, and Student* (Phila., 1851).

The first institutions which sought to place a major emphasis on the dissemination of knowledge of technology were not the schools but societies in the pattern of learned societies; most important for the Americans was the London Society of Arts. On this help and stimulus, the recent microfilm edition of The American Correspondence of the Royal Society of Arts, London, 1755–1840, by Micro Methods (London, 1963) is more helpful than Derek Hudson and Kenneth W. Luckhurst, *The Royal Society of Arts, 1754–1954* (London, 1954). Little has been written on the American societies that followed this pattern, although they are lightly covered in Brooke Hindle, *The Pursuit of Science in Revolutionary America* (Chapel Hill, 1956). The manufacturing societies of the early Republic require still more attention. Although thin on these and on engineering societies, Ralph S. Bates provides related help in his *Scientific Societies in the United States* (2nd edn., N. Y., 1958).

The mechanics institutes represent another stage of development which has been much more satisfactorily studied for England than for the United States. Charles Alpheus Bennett, *History of Manual and Industrial Education up to 1870* (Peoria, 1926), gives attention to the mechanics institutes, and especially to the Franklin Institute, but this constitutes a minor part of the book. The details of the development of the Franklin Institute, the most important of the mechanics institutes, are to some extent revealed in its *Journal* which dates from 1826. Bruce Sinclair, at the Case Institute of Technology, is writing a doctoral dissertation on the history of the Franklin Institute.

Another level of institutional development was attained with the founding of the Smithsonian Institution in 1846; its initial impact on technology was negligible, but in time it did become significant. Perhaps still best on its early days is George Brown Goode, *The Smithsonian Institution, 1846–1896: The History of Its First Half Century* (Washington, 1897).

The approach to a more regular and ordered instruction in the elements of technology, which had little beginning before the Revolution, immediately called into question existing principles and the extent to which science was or could be the basis of technological instruction. Almost as a matter of Baconian faith, the Americans had assumed that science, or orderly principle, underlay all practical pursuits. Yet this was not entirely self-evident, nor was it easy to find the principles sought. The early relationships between science and technology in Europe have called forth some thoughtful considerations. Somewhat contrasting views are presented in Charles C. Gillispie, "The Discovery of the Leblanc Process," *Isis*, 48 (1957), 152–67, and Robert E. Schofield, "The Industrial Orientation of Science in the Lunar Society of Birmingham," *Isis*, 48 (1957), 408–15. A similar contrast of a limited versus a more positive role of science is offered in Donald Fleming, "Latent Heat and the Invention of the Watt Engine," *Isis*, 43 (1952), 3–5, and Milton Kerker, "Science and the Steam Engine," *Technology and Culture*, 2 (1961), 381–90. A recent reconsideration has produced commentary and two articles: Derek J. de Solla Price, "Is Technology Historically Independent of Science? A Study in Statistical Historiography," *Technology and Culture*, 6 (1965), 553–68 and Robert P. Multhauf, "Sal Ammoniac: A Case History in Industrialization," *ibid.*, 569–86. There are no similar inquiries of the American experience.

While mechanics in the republican period were being trained in the new machine shops and practical civil engineers were being trained on the great canal projects, institutions for formal technical education were arising. Calhoun, *The American Civil Engineer*, brilliantly describes those which trained civil engineers and encouraged the development of a self-conscious profession. The original schools were the United States Military Academy, Rensselaer Polytechnic Institute, and Alden Partridge's School (later Norwich University). The existing histories of these institutions help only slightly in picturing the process of technical education: Forman's *West Point*; Henry B. Nason, ed., *Biographical Record of the Officers and Graduates of the Rensselaer Polytechnic Institute, 1824–1886* (Troy, 1887); and William A. Ellis, ed., *Norwich University, 1819–1911*, 3 vols. (Montpelier, Vt., 1911). Much more revealing are the textbooks used: at West Point, Mahan's two works; and at Rensselaer, Amos Eaton's *Art without Science: or Mensuration, Surveying and Engineering, Divested of the Speculative Principles and Technical Language of Mathematics* (Albany, 1830) and *Prodromus of a Practical Treatise on the Mathematical Arts* (Troy, 1838). Eaton's books were practical, but a non-scientific veneer covered over his methods—and looked in the wrong direction.

Using an approach they imagined to be different, some contemporaries sought strenuously to apply science to practice for students, machinists, and engineers. Even when they did not succeed, the books they published usually announced the application of science. First among these enthusiasts was Jacob Bigelow, whose efforts followed his appointment to the Rumford Chair at Harvard, established for "the application of the sciences to the useful arts." He had to start at the beginning, but in his *Inaugural Address* (Boston, 1817) he charted a possible course. His lecture series constituted a survey of technology which he published in expanded form as *Elements of Technology* (Boston, 1829) and expanded still further in *The Useful Arts*, 2 vols. (N. Y., 1847).

James Cutbush, chemistry professor at the University of Pennsylvania, worked many years at efforts to aid practicing manufacturers by making scientific principles available to them. Most general of his offerings is *The American Artist's Manual, or Dictionary of Practical Knowledge in the Application of Philosophy to the Arts and Manufactures*, 2 vols. (Phila., 1814). He also wrote treatises on the practical uses of hydrometers, the applications of chemistry, and "pyrotechny" based on chemical principles.

For "practical men" rather than for his college students, James Renwick of Columbia College wrote *Applications of the Science of Mechanics to Practical Purposes* (N. Y., 1844); he is also responsible for a basic college text. Campbell Morfit's books on soap and candle making, perfumery, and tanning also represent efforts to apply science, in this case chemistry. Alonzo Potter, *The Principles of Science Applied to the Domestic and Mechanic Arts* (Boston, 1840), is not only a similar effort but also a first-rate survey.

At the Franklin Institute, Walter R. Johnson wrote a number of pieces that are almost like recent engineers' reports. Johnson, who practiced as a civil and mining engineer, served as professor of mechanics and natural philosophy at the Institute and later as professor of chemistry and natural philosophy in the Medical Department of the University of Pennsylvania; he spent his life trying to apply science to practical purposes. In addition to his *Report . . . on American Coals*, his publications include: "Observations on the Relations between Rolling and Dragging Friction," *Experiments on Rail-Roads* (Baltimore, 1829), 1–12; *Notes on the Use of Anthracite in the Manufacture of Iron* (Boston, 1841); and, in another vein, a significant analysis of patents in *A Lecture on the Mechanical Industry and the Inventive Genius of America* (Baltimore, 1849).

Through much of this literature, specifically in Eaton, Morfit, Potter, and—despite his assertions—Bigelow, there is an anti-intellectual and anti-scientific impulse in the desire to adapt science to "practical men" by eliminating mathematics and as much of principles as possible. At the same time, most of the authors were moving in the opposite direction as they sensed the need to find a mathematical basis for technology, a view which ultimately took hold of their better efforts. One of the finest examples of a mathematically based building block for engineering education is the textbook of William Barton Rogers, a professor of natural philosophy and chemistry first at the College of William and Mary, then at the University of Virginia, and later the founder of the Massachusetts Institute of Technology: *An Elementary Treatise on the Strength of Materials* (Charlottesville, 1838).

K. America and Europe

The relationship in technology between America and Europe was continuous but complex and shifting in its character. The initial process was entirely one of transferring the bases of European technology across the Atlantic. This current, of course, never ended, even though a countercurrent, carrying American technological ideas and innovations back to Europe, became strong toward the end of the early period. The movement of technology to America, however, was very different in different sectors of industry, and it altered significantly in origin and content during the colonial and early national era.

Several good scholars have recently given recognition to the significance of the transfer of technology to America. First in importance is Norman B. Wilkinson, "Brandywine Borrowings from European Technology," *Technology and Culture*, 4 (1963), 1–13, a presentation of several strikingly different examples drawn from the study of Delaware and Pennsylvania. He makes one of his leading sources available in Harold B. Hancock and Norman B. Wilkinson, "Joshua Gilpin: An American Manufacturer in England and Wales, 1795–1801," Newcomen Society, *Transactions*, 33 (1961), 15–28, 57–66. Eugene S. Ferguson, "On the Origin and Development of American Mechanical 'Know-How,'" *Midcontinent American Studies Journal*, 3 (1962), 3–16, offers an imaginative examination tied to many specific instances. A different approach, a study in depth of one episode, is Carroll W. Pursell, Jr., "Thomas Digges and William Pearce: An Example of the Transit of Technology," *William and Mary Quarterly*, 3d Ser., 21 (1964), 551–60.

Related studies have been made, primarily by economic historians and students of population movement; the weakness of most of them is that they deal in gross statistics and do not sufficiently distinguish between those who tended machines and those who designed and built them. Most pertinent is Herbert Heaton, "The Industrial Immigrant in the United States, 1783–1812," APS, *Proceedings*, 45 (1951), 519–27. Best of the larger-scale studies is Rowland Tappan Berthoff, *British Immigrants in Industrial America, 1790–1950* (Cambridge, Mass., 1953). A good study of the parallel movement of British technology to the Continent is W. O. Henderson, *Britain and Industrial Europe, 1750–1870* (Liverpool, 1954).

Among contemporary materials giving some insight into the process of moving mechanics and technological ideas across the Atlantic are the emigrants' guidebooks, compiled and edited by Charlotte Erickson and now made conveniently available by Micro Methods in microfilm: *Emigrants Guides and Pamphlets* (London, 1965). Those written by emigrants who contributed to the improvement of technology have special relevance: Thomas Cooper, *Some Information Respecting America* (London, 1794), and Mathew Carey, *Reflections on the Subject of Emigration* (Phila., 1826). One of the best-known views of the transfer of technology is found in the "Letters of Phineas Bond, British Consul at Philadelphia, to the Foreign Office of Great Britain, 1787, 1788, 1789," American Historical Association, *Annual Report for 1896*, Vol. I (Washington, 1897), although they are only a selection of the Public Records Office reports.

The overwhelming dependence upon Britain in the early transfer of technology is unquestionable. However, as the need arose to train engineers and mechanics in a more regular manner and to move ahead with planned technological improvements, the deficiencies of empirical methods used by British immigrants, and often reflected in British manuals, became more apparent. The Americans reached increasingly for the principles, and they often found them more readily in French works and finally in German ones. This process has led to a curious distortion, represented best in the much praised study by Ralph R. Shaw, *Engineering Books Available in America Prior to 1830* (N. Y., 1933). Shaw finds that American libraries have a proportionately better representation of French engineering books published before 1830 than of

English works. This does not reflect greater dependence on French engineering in that period—but only the movement, mostly after that date, to base engineering on principle. Similarly, Stephen P. Timoshenko's fine *History of Strength of Materials* (N. Y., 1953) underplays early dependence on British trial tables because he traces primarily the development of principle and theory. The early British pattern was not replaced in the United States by a theoretical commitment as great as that manifested by the French. A related article by Brooke Hindle, entitled "British v. French Influence on American Technology in the Early Republic," will be published in the forthcoming *Proceedings* of the XIth International Congress of the History of Science.

L. *Patents and Invention*

Invention occupies a peculiarly central position in the history of technology; indeed, the course of technology is not infrequently sketched in terms of leaps from one great invention to the next. This concept of invention as a stroke of genius underlay the patent system and was bolstered by its influence. The two topics are closely intertwined, and both are deeply involved in current reassessments and reexaminations.

This view of invention has left a trail of works which seek to identify and glorify early American inventors—often running along the path blazed by Samuel Smiles. A clear example is Philip G. Hubert, Jr., *Inventors* ("Men of Achievement Series") (N. Y., 1893), which enters a strong plea to accord more honor to the American heroes of invention than to Napoleon Bonaparte. Less biographical but equally bound by this concept are Edward W. Byrn, *Progress of Inventions in the Nineteenth Century* (N. Y., 1904), and Bradley A. Fiske, *Invention, the Master-Key to Progress* (N. Y., 1921). More recently, L. Sprague de Camp, *The Heroic Age of American Invention* (Garden City, 1961), makes clear the support that the heroic view of invention received from the larger role of the single individual in early nineteenth-century technology.

A highly structured, sociological approach to invention was more popular in the 1930's than it is today; it is most clearly represented in the writings of S. Collum Gilfillan, *The Sociology of Invention* (Chicago, 1935) and *Inventing the Ship* (Chicago, 1935). Similar in set is the less imaginative, questionnaire-based Joseph Rossman, *The Psychology of the Inventor* (Washington, 1931). The most promising of current sociological investigators does not even concern himself primarily with technology; yet Robert K. Merton makes points of great relevance to invention. Most accessible are his "Singletons and Multiples in Scientific Discovery," APS, *Proceedings*, 105 (1961), 470–92, and "Priorities in Scientific Discovery," *American Sociological Review*, 22 (1957), 635–59.

The most active area of interest in invention at present is among the economic historians, who have turned their attention this way in the wake of their concern for economic growth. One of the most influential of the general works in this category is W. W. Rostow, *The Process of Economic Growth* (N. Y., 1952), but more pointed is Douglass C. North, *The Economic Growth of the United States, 1790–1860* (Englewood Cliffs, N. J., 1961), an excellent analysis which carefully weighs technology and fits invention into the formula but does not make it the dominant factor. Stuart Bruchey, *The Roots of American Economic Growth, 1607–1861: An Essay in Social Causation* (N. Y., 1965), gives a larger role to technological invention. Also from the background of economic history is John Jewkes, David Sawers, and Richard Stillerman, *The Sources of Invention* (London, 1958). Although concerned primarily with the present, this work reviews interpretations of invention and gives some attention to the early American period.

Most directly on target in time and topic are two excellent recent inquiries. H. J. Habakkuk, *American and British Technology in the Nineteenth Century: The Search for Labour-Saving Inventions* (Cambridge, Eng., 1962), is a pioneering work which combines theoretical economics with the historical study of technology, concentrating upon the lone point of labor-saving machinery. This remains a very important question, and both his analysis and the information he adduces are valuable resources. W. Paul Strassman, *Risk and Technological Innovation: American Manufacturing Methods during the Nineteenth Century* (Ithaca, 1959), is a broader study of selected fields of technology, three of them relevant to the early nineteenth century. A clearer presentation than Habakkuk's, this is a great aid to understanding, especially of the whole process of which invention is a part.

Patents were not of much importance on the colonial scene, and traditional accounts of the American patent system err much when they imply a continuing expansion of patents after the first award to Joseph Jencks in 1646. In fact, many colonies never granted a patent and none granted many. Patents are primarily a post-Revolutionary story. The expansion of numbers of patents was begun by the states in the 1780's; in 1790 the Federal Patent Act went into effect; from 1793 to 1836 a mere registry system prevailed; and from 1836, proof of novelty, originality, and utility were required.

Now and formerly, there has been a sense of the historical importance of the patent system and of patent records, intact since the fire of 1836, but little organized research has so far penetrated these enormously valuable resources. Useful historical reviews are available in P. J. Federico, ed., "Outline of the History of the United States Patent Office," *Journal of the Patent Office Society*, 18 (1936), No. 7, pp. 1–251, and Levin H. Campbell, *The Patent System of the United States* (Washington, 1891). Lists of patents and guides abound; among the starting points are: [U.S. Patent Office], *List of Patents . . . 1790 to 1847* (Washington, 1847), and M. D. Leggett, comp., *Subject Matter Index of Patents . . . 1790 to 1873*, 3 vols. (Washington, 1874). *The Journal of the Franklin Institute* was not always able to get the desired patent data, but published much of it from 1826 to 1836; for those years it is often the best source.

Key commentaries on invention, involving historical summaries and evaluations, are found in the series of annual reports of the Commissioner of Patents: for example, *Report of the Commissioner of Patents . . . during the Year 1843*, 28th Cong., 1st Sess., Senate Doc. No. 150 (Washington, 1844). A large number of polemic pieces surrounded the patenting process; the explosions of Oliver Evans are especially apt: *Patent Right Oppression Exposed; or, Knavery Detected* (Philadelphia, 1813), *Oliver Evans to his Counsel* (n.p., 1817), and *Exposition of Part of the Patent Law* (n.p., 1816). Contemporary reviews of the process are Thomas G. Fessenden, *Essay on the Law of Patents* (Boston, 1810), and Willard Phillips, *Law of Patents* (Boston, 1837).

Alf K. Berle and L. Sprague de Camp discuss patterns of attack and defense of the patent system in *Inventions, Patents, and Their Management* (Princeton, 1959). In 1925 Floyd L. Vaughn launched an attack in his *Economics of our Patent System* (N. Y.), but his 1956 version is much less critical. A strong recent defense is Anthony William Deller, "Social and Economic Impact of Patents," *Journal of the Patent Office Society*, 46 (1964), 424–57. The last of these is the most historical, but all present viewpoints worth keeping in mind in investigating early technology.

M. *Technology in American History*

Many of the works cited above, especially in the preceding section, constitute critiques of the role of technology. Most of them evaluate technology with respect to some other specific area of study, such as the economy. There have, in addition, been efforts to consider technology in relation to the whole of history, in relation to the whole life of mankind, and in relation to many of the important, separate aspects of life. Even those not specifically directed toward the interpretation of early American history must be considered by historians of the technology of this period.

One of the major critical surveys of technology in history, which still retains its stimulating, disquieting character, is Lewis Mumford, *Technics and Civilization* (N. Y., 1934). This is a highly interpretive review with heavy value judgments made primarily from social and aesthetic viewpoints. His *Art and Technics* (N. Y., 1952) is a series of lectures which comprise more limited reflection. Siegfried Giedion, *Mechanization Takes Command* (N. Y., 1954), attains a somewhat similar philosophical overview but concentrates upon the recent past.

There are no closely parallel examinations of American technology alone, but Daniel J. Boorstin, *The Image, or What Happened to the American Dream* (N. Y., 1962), represents a critique of what appear to be the worst results of technology and mechanization. In the traditional form of chronological history, he applies equal imagination to the examination of the initial period of mechanization in the second volume of his work, *The Americans: The National Experience* (N. Y., 1965). John A. Kouwenhoven, *Made in America: The Arts in Modern Civilization* (Garden City, 1948), analyzes design of technological products as an expression of popular taste.

Philosophical evaluations of technology and its results were also a part of the early American period; examples are presented in Richard S. Rosenbloom, "Some 19th-Century Analyses of Mechanization," *Technology and Culture*, 5 (1964), 489–511. The first British enthusiast of mechanization to have wide influence in the United States was Andrew Ure, *The Philosophy of Manufactures* (London, 1835). Among American writings on the Utopian possibilities inherent in mechanization are Thomas Ewbank, *The World a Workshop* (N. Y., 1855), and J. A. Etzler, *The Paradise within the Reach of all Men without Labor, by Powers of Nature and Machinery* (Pittsburgh, 1833). Etzler, however, is remembered chiefly because his work was reviewed by Thoreau and, according to the legend, demolished (*Democratic Review*, 13 [1843], 451–63).

In fact, not a few American literary figures were saddened and some spoke out against the threat they saw in mechanization. This story is unfolded very sensitively in Leo Marx, *The Machine in the Garden: Technology and the Pastoral Ideal in America* (N. Y., 1964), a major interpretive synthesis. A vignette within this scheme is offered in Leo B. Levy, "Hawthorne's 'Canal Boat': An Experiment in Landscape," *American Quarterly*, 16 (1964), 211–15.

Historians have usually avoided involvement in the great philosophical questions when they study technology. John U. Nef in *War and Human Progress: An Essay on the Rise of Industrial Civilization* (Cambridge, Mass., 1950) is an exception; he concludes that the industrial state was purchased at the expense of the decline of the human mind. More comfortable is a familiar work in American history which begins with the early American period and securely ties technology to one of the great interpretive themes in American history—the frontier movement. Walter P. Webb, *The Great Plains* (N. Y., 1931), has not always been placed in the right light; the preliminary sketch for it was entitled "The Great Plains and the Industrial Revolution" (in James F. Willard and Colin B. Goodykoontz, eds., *The Trans-Mississippi West* [Boulder, 1930]). Hugo A. Meier presents a refreshingly direct confrontation of the interrelationships between American political and technological ideals in his "Technology and Democracy, 1800–1860," *Mississippi Valley Historical Review*, 43 (1957), 618–40. Although more peripherally, perceptive historians have frequently acknowledged the role of technology in some of the greatest themes in American history, among them urbanization, immigration, and economic expansion.

The central role of technology in American history has been recognized by only a few general historians who have devoted special study to it. American economic history textbooks give attention to technology in a measure that has increased with the increased interest in economic growth. General American history textbooks often include a few technological episodes, but their sensitivity to technology remains altogether inadequate.

A DIRECTORY

OF ARTIFACT

COLLECTIONS

by Lucius F. Ellsworth

I. INTRODUCTION

The aesthetic significance of such three-dimensional objects as glassware, fabrics, pottery, lighting devices, and spinning wheels has always interested historians of art, culture, and society. But scholars have generally overlooked the importance of using artifacts in conjunction with a wide variety of the more traditional research resources in their study of early American technology. Instead of their aesthetic form, the historian of technology can view three-dimensional objects in terms of their external appearance, their composition or internal structure, and the technical know-how associated with making and using objects.

From an examination of the physical appearance of objects, historians of technology have been able to compare the external form of several objects of the same general type but from different time periods or places of origin, and thus to observe the development of the artifact from, for example, a crude but useful hand tool to a highly perfected machine. In some instances small refinements within the more general progression are readily apparent. The evolution of spinning equipment from the distaff through hand spinning wheels to the eighteenth- and early nineteenth-century machines of Richard Arkwright and Samuel Crompton provides a good example of both possibilities. The historian may also discover that such artifacts as pottery-making tools changed little during several generations of use.

Historians of technology have also recently begun to analyze the composition of the materials used to form an object. Advances in such techniques as optical spectroscopy now permit relatively accurate period dating of specific metal objects through the identification of trace elements peculiar to a particular level of metallurgy. Although most of these techniques are still in the experimental stage in such programs as the Andelot-Copeland Museum Science Project, a cooperative venture of the Henry Francis du Pont Winterthur Museum and the University of Delaware, their value for both the museum conservator and the historian is already apparent.

When external appearances, material composition, and written descriptions prove insufficient for a thorough understanding of a technical process, then the know-how associated with making and using objects becomes important. By observing carefully a demonstration of a technique by a skilled craftsman, a person can more easily grasp the technology involved. But historians and other observers must realize that a process demonstration has value only if the representation is authentic. The importance of the know-how of technology is indicated by the fact that no one in this country is able today to make wooden barrels by hand even though suitable tools abound and cooperage was once one of the most practiced crafts in America.

Writings on Artifact Collections

Since the Second World War a few historians increasingly have studied various types of three-dimensional objects in order to understand better the total significance of their topics. The results of their researches are now appearing in book form. Besides providing an excellent account of the structural art of building, Carl W. Condit, in *American Building Art: The Nineteenth Century* and *American Building Art: The Twentieth Century* (N. Y., 1961), suggests additional insights into the society that created the buildings. More recently Alan Gowans, in *Images of American Living* (Phila., 1964), analyzes furniture and architecture as cultural expressions of American civilization. Through the study of objects and the society which produced the objects, Gowans observes the patterns of man's progressive conquest over nature, of social change, of changing concepts of the nature of art and architecture, and, finally, of evolving economic and social democracy. That Gowans' technique reflects his training as an art historian should not detract from the value of his approach for historians who are attempting to relate technology to the whole of human experience.

Directly relevant to the study of pre-Civil War American technology is Charles Hummel's forthcoming *With Hammer in Hand: The Dom-*

iny Craftsmen of East Hampton. While cataloguing the wood and metal working tools in the Dominy Workshop at the Henry Francis du Pont Winterthur Museum, Hummel also traces the economic and social significance of these craftsmen and analyzes the products of the shop. This well-illustrated publication should clearly indicate to historians the value of studying artifacts in conjunction with manuscripts and printed sources.

Various types of three-dimensional objects should interest historians of technology. Of paramount importance are those artifacts which were used for securing raw materials, for converting raw materials to usable products, for augmenting human power, for aiding and increasing man's mobility, and for furthering man's scientific knowledge about himself and the universe. The physical remains of such structures as homes, factories, and bridges illustrate both engineering developments as well as building materials. Although of lesser importance, the almost endless number and variety of surviving finished products can still prove helpful to the researcher in technology.

Historians desiring to study artifacts face the problem of thousands of objects widely scattered throughout the United States in private collections, company museums, public museums, public restorations, and historical societies. Obtaining knowledge of the existence of private collections is the most difficult for the historian. Often his only recourse is to leaf painstakingly through the issues of *Antiques*, or *The Chronicle* of the Early American Industries Association, or the less professional but still useful *Antiques Journal, Antique Dealer and Collector's Guide,* and *Antique Collector.* All of these publications deal generally with the collecting of both foreign and domestic antiques. For information on specific types of private artifact collections, such magazines as *The Rushlight*, the *Bulletin* of the Pewter Collectors Club of America, and *Gun Report* can be of limited value. Researchers will quickly discover that the indexes to these serial publications are of little assistance in compiling catalogues of relevant collections.

A variety of lists and guides to company museums, public museums, public restorations, and historical societies published in recent years substantially aids the historian of technology in ferreting out likely depositories of relevant artifacts. An indispensable book, which lists 4,956 United States and Canada museums by geographic locations, by an alphabetical list, and by category (i.e., art, science, company, national and state agencies, and specialized subjects), is E. O. Christensen, *Museum Directory of the United States and Canada* (Washington, 1961, revised 1965). In addition to an excellent subject index, this book contains brief sketches of the nature of each museum's collections.

Another publication, Herbert and Marjorie Katz, *Museums, U.S.A.* (Garden City, N. Y., 1965), although written more for the layman than the professional researcher, combines survey information about the historical development of art, science, history, and children's museums in the United States with a geographical listing of institutions based essentially upon Christensen's book. The most rewarding parts of the book are the concise descriptions of individual exhibits, but historians should note that these describe interpretive displays rather than collections of artifacts.

"Museums of Science and Technology," *Technology and Culture,* 4 (1963), 142–47, merely cites by name several hundred private and public museums. Another shorter but annotated list appears in George Sarton, *A Guide to the History of Science* (Waltham, Mass., 1952), pages 280–89. Historians can glean additional information about museum collections from *Technology and Culture,* 6 (1965), No. 1, an issue devoted to museums of technology.

Determining more precisely the nature of these collections from secondary sources proves even more difficult because few museums have published catalogues of their holdings. In addition to the brochures which most museums issue for the general public, a few institutions have also published booklets and in several instances books which describe specific parts of their holdings or special exhibitions. Since few bibliographies exist, learning about these museum publications is a formidable task. Jane Clapp, *Museum Publications,* 2 vols. (New York, 1962), is a noteworthy though inadequate attempt. As Eugene S. Ferguson has suggested, someone needs to devise a simple, straight-forward, yet comprehensive bibliography of museum publications.

Museums specializing in the decorative arts have far surpassed history museums, company museums, and historical societies both in the number and caliber of publications pertaining to their own collections and exhibits. Regrettably for the historian of technology, such aesthetically pleasing artifacts as silver, pottery, and furniture often seem to outweigh in importance the supposedly less attractive tools and machines used by craftsmen to make refined end products. Even less has been written about collections of heavy machinery and animal-powered vehicles commonly used in the United States before the middle of the nineteenth century. Perhaps the demonstrated interest of private collectors and laymen in "art" objects explains what appears to the historian of technology to be an imbalance in museum literature. This is not to say that these popular publications are not valuable; it is only to say that they do not meet the basic needs of researchers in technology.

As previously mentioned, the study of finished products can prove rewarding to historians of technology. The following are useful guides to consult: Alice Winchester, ed., *The Antiques Treasury of Furniture and Other Decorative Arts at Winterthur, Williamsburg, Sturbridge, Ford Museum, Cooperstown, Deerfield, Shelburne* (N. Y., 1959); John A. H. Sweeney, *Winterthur Illustrated* (Wilmington, 1963), 177 pp.; [Cooper Union Museum], *An Illustrated Survey of the Collection* (N. Y., n.d.); "European and American Glass in the Newark Museum's Collection," *The Museum,* 7 (Newark Museum, 1955), Nos. 3–4; [Newark Museum], *An Introduction to Silver: Catalogue of an Exhibition* (Newark, 1954); Martha Gandy Fales, *American Silver in the Henry Francis du Pont Winterthur Museum* (Wilmington, 1958); John Graham, *American Pewter* (N. Y., 1949); Helen McKearin, *American Historical Flasks* (N. Y., 1953); Jerome Strauss, *Glass Drinking Vessels* (N. Y., 1955); [Corning Museum of Glass], *Guide to the Collections: A Chronology of Glassmaking from Ancient Egypt to the Beginning of the 20th Century* (Corning, N. Y., 1958); *Kirk Silver in U. S. Museums* (Baltimore, 1961); *Antiques at Williamsburg* (N. Y., 1953); and *Popular Antiques at the Henry Ford Museum* (N. Y., 1958).

Only a few catalogues of objects more relevant to the study of technology have appeared. M. V. Brewington, *The Peabody Museum Collection of Navigating Instruments with Notes on Their Makers* (Salem, 1963), serves a dual role by providing authoritative material about this museum's excellent holdings of instruments and by serving as a model for other museums when planning catalogues.

Silvio A. Bedini, *Early American Scientific Instruments and their Makers* (U. S. National Museum, *Bulletin,* No. 231 [Washington, 1964]), 184 pp., lists in the first section early American instrument makers and some of their products now in both private and public collections. In another part of this work Bedini enumerates by maker and user the collection of early American scientific instruments and related material in the United States National Museum. The omissions in the first edition hopefully will be supplied in the forthcoming revised edition. Other publications by the Smithsonian Institution, including *Proceedings of the United States National Museum* and *United States National Museum Bulletin,* occasionally mention specific artifact holdings. Historians of technology should especially note *Bulletin* No. 280, *Contributions from the Museum of History and Technology,* since most of these articles are based upon printed and manuscript material and three-dimensional objects at the United States National Museum.

Several specialized catalogues or lists have appeared, i.e., George

Griffenhagen, "International List of Pharmacy Museums" in Glenn Sonnedecker, *Kremers and Urdangs History of Pharmacy*, 3d edn. (Philadelphia, 1963), pp. 384–95; *American Pharmacy Historical Collections* (Washington, 1965); *List of Steam Locomotives on Display in the United States* (Washington, 1965); [Mütter Museum of the College of Physicians], *Accessions Catalogue* (Phila., n.d.); *Winchester Gun Museum* (N. Y., n.d.); *Musical Instruments at Yale* (New Haven, n.d.); Frederick C. Holtz and Frances S. Ridgley, *Clocks from the Hunter Collection* [Illinois State Museum] (Normal, Ill., 1957); *Fire Engines on Parade; The H. V. Smith Museum Collection* (N. Y., 1956); [Suffolk Museum], *Carriage Catalogue* (Stony Brook, Long Island, N. Y., 1954); Robert E. Peabody, *American Sailing Ships: The Ship Model Collection at the Addison Gallery of American Art* (Andover, Mass., 1961); and Henry Spector, ed., *The Ship Model Collection of the Commercial Museum* (Phila., 1964).

Shelburne Museum has issued a series of booklets describing its collections. Of special interest are: Lilian Baker Carlisle, *The Carriages at Shelburne Museum* (Shelburne, Vt., 1956); Frank H. Wildung, *Woodworking Tools at Shelburne Museum* (Shelburne, Vt., 1957); and *Blacksmith and Wheelwright Tools at Shelburne Museum* (Shelburne, Vt., 1961). Wildung's book is especially well illustrated.

Mariners Museum: A History and Guide (Newport News, Va., 1950); Louis C. Jones, *Cooperstown* (Cooperstown, N. Y., 1953); Ralph Nading Hill and Lilian Baker Carlisle, *The Story of Shelburne Museum* (Shelburne, Vt., 1955); and Walter Muir Whitehill, *Independent Historical Societies: An Inquiry into their Research and Publication Functions and Financial Future* (Boston, 1962), primarily contain historical information with a few notes on the types of collections at each institution. Some emphasize the history; others emphasize the artifact.

Other authors with varying degrees of success have combined descriptions of the artifact with an explanation of either the construction or the functional purposes of the object. Henry C. Mercer's *Ancient Carpenters' Tools* (Doylestown, Pa., 1960), and *The Bible in Iron* (Doylestown, Pa., 1960), still stand as the chief sources of information about woodworking tools and stove plates, though the revised editions could contain a better grade of illustrations. These books also indicate some of the immense artifact holdings of the Bucks County Historical Society which historians of technology have not yet carefully studied.

Typical of the how-to-do books are: [Baltimore Museum of Art], *Glass Through Time: Essay on Glass Making* (Baltimore, 1953); [Los

Angeles County Museum of History, Science and Art], *Art of the Weaver* (Los Angeles, 1954); [Textile Museum], *Craft Habits, Work Shop Notes* (Washington, D.C., n.d.), Nos. 19, 20; [Cleveland Museum of Art], *Two Thousand Years of Silk Weaving* (Cleveland, n.d.); [Walters Art Gallery], *History of Bookbinding, 1525–1950* (Baltimore, 1957); and the Williamsburg Craft Series, including August Klapper, *The Printer in 18th Century Williamsburg* (Williamsburg, 1964); William de Matteo, *The Silversmith in 18th Century Williamsburg* (Williamsburg, 1956); Lloyd Payne, *The Miller in 18th Century Virginia* (Williamsburg, 1958); and C. Clement Samford, *The Bookbinder in 18th Century Williamsburg* (Williamsburg, 1964).

Occasionally, writers have attempted to place objects into a larger economic, social, or technological framework. Some of the Old Sturbridge Village Booklet Series reflect careful research and clear writing: these include Catherine Fennelly, *Textiles in New England, 1790–1840* (Sturbridge, Mass., 1961); Catherine Fennelly, *New England Clocks at Old Sturbridge Village: The J. Cheney Wells Collection* (Sturbridge, Mass., 1955); Kenneth M. Wilson, *Glass in New England* (Sturbridge, Mass., 1959); and Lura W. Watkins, *Early New England Pottery* (Sturbridge, Mass., 1959). Harold Warp, *A History of Man's Progress from 1830 to the Present* [Harold Warp Pioneer Village] (Minden, Nebr., n.d.), has some relevant information.

Historians of technology can consult the Historic American Buildings Survey which not only inventories historic buildings and sites but also preserves architectural drawings, pictures, and other documentary material about these structures and sites. Begun in the 1930's under the sponsorship of the federal government, the project unfortunately was curtailed during and after World War II. Responsibility for the revitalized venture now rests with the National Park Service, the American Institute of Architects, the National Trust for Historic Preservation, and the Library of Congress. For additional information researchers should consult two published guides to the archives of this project: *Catalog of the Measured Drawings and Photographs of the Survey in the Library of Congress* (Washington, 1941), and *Catalog Supplement* (Washington, 1959).

Scope and Intent of the Directory

The preceding bibliography of published museum guides and catalogues, though certainly not exhaustive, indicates the acute shortage of printed materials about artifact collections relevant to the study of early American technology. To help overcome this obstacle to research, the author has prepared a listing of some of the public and company collections which could prove useful for historians of technology. From the inception of the project no attempt was made to compile an exhaustive directory of public institutions and company museums, or even to try to enumerate the thousands of private collections. The purpose of this directory, therefore, is to describe the types of objects, including accurate models of artifacts, a researcher could expect to find in several representative public and company collections in the United States, and to list a few additional museums, historical sites, and historical societies which have similar holdings.

The information in the directory has been compiled from 168 responses to 380 questionnaires mailed by the author to public museums, restorations, company museums, and historical societies; from surveys by the author of the holdings at the Smithsonian Institution, the Franklin Institute, the Bucks County Historical Society, the Henry Ford Museum, Old Sturbridge Village, Saugus Ironworks Restoration, the Old Slater Mill, Mystic Seaport, Merrimack Valley Textile Museum, Peabody Museum of Salem, Massachusetts, Essex Institute, New York State Historical Association, Colonial Williamsburg, Inc., Jamestown Visitor Center at the Colonial National Historical Park, Henry Francis du Pont Winterthur Museum, Old Salem, Inc., and Hagley Museum; from the files of the Registrar's Office at the Hagley Museum; and from the helpful suggestions of museum personnel, particularly Minor Wine Thomas of the New York State Historical Association.

The reader should be aware of the pitfalls inherent in the use of the questionnaire method of compiling information. Phrasing questions that the respondents clearly comprehend and uniformly interpret proves exceedingly difficult. An uneven quality of responses comes in part from this lack of understanding the question. Another factor is the viewpoint of each person answering the questions. Viewing a collection objectively can be extremely hard for a person who has closely worked with the artifacts for any period of time. The usefulness of the responses also varies because the information depends upon the reliability of the records concerning each object. Some curators diligently seek out accurate data; others haphazardly accept evidence. In selecting institutions to receive questionnaires, I have possibly overlooked some collections which should have been included, thereby contributing to the uneven nature of the results. In order to counteract some of these tendencies, I have checked the responses with available printed sources of information and with other museum personnel. I am ultimately responsible, however, for the shortcomings of the directory. That the directory mentions neither private holdings nor some of the smaller public depositories and lacks an exhaustive description of the collections indicates a need for the expansion of the current project.

While preparing the directory, three characteristics of the collections surveyed became increasingly apparent to me. Each characteristic indicates both a need and an opportunity for research by historians of technology and professional museologists. The first is the large number of objects in public museums which most scholars and even antiquarians generally have ignored in their studies through oversight or lack of knowledge of the existence of the collection. Since many museums with limited display space are inclined to show only certain types of objects that will have large public appeal, the majority of their collections often remain in almost inaccessible storage areas. The immense holdings of the Bucks County Historical Society furnish an excellent example. Although this museum has one of the finest collections of pre-steam-power tools in the United States, few scholars besides the founder, Henry Mercer, have carefully studied the objects. The second characteristic is the almost endless number of artifacts in small historical societies and museums and in the collections of private individuals about which few people know. Private individuals and companies still own some of the very best technological collections, especially in the case of such artifacts as firearms and lighting devices. Scant information about these collections makes the job of the thorough researcher even more difficult. The third characteristic of American collections, the dearth of known artifacts in certain areas such as papermaking, tanning, mining, and the manufacturing of chemicals, severely handicaps historians working on topics in these fields. Perhaps an organization like the Society for the History of Technology or the Early American Industries Association could prepare a catalog of the location of artifacts and then publish the findings.

The lack of any unified method of identifying and describing objects also creates problems for researchers when they analyze or compare three-dimensional objects. Some institution, professional association, or government agency should initiate a pilot project aimed at determining the feasibility of unified cataloguing of technological artifacts. If such an approach proves practical from a classification and a monetary viewpoint, an attempt should be made to extend the project to incorporate the major museum holdings of related objects. The researcher would then have readily available more accurate information. Admittedly such an undertaking would require a large well-trained staff and the sizable expenditure of funds; however, the benefits for all types of historical research would be correspondingly large.

Artifacts directly related to early American technology exist in abundance; the challenge of carefully studying these objects and of interpreting their significance in a broader historical framework now lies with the museologist, the general historian, and the historian of technology.

II. RAW MATERIAL PRODUCTION

A. Mining and Quarrying

1. *Smithsonian Institution, Washington, D. C.*—A fairly complete set of anthracite tools of a type used before 1850, a model of an early coal crusher (ca. 1844), safety lamps, and a variety of mine articles.

2. *Bucks County Historical Society, Doylestown, Pa.*—The Mercer Museum of the Society has an extensive group of such hand tools as picks, sledges, chisels, bits, miners' lamps, and a hand ore crusher.

3. *State Historical Society of Wisconsin, Madison, Wis.*—A fairly representative collection of hand tools used in lead mining.

4. *Other institutions.*—Canal Museum, Syracuse, N. Y.; New Almaden Museum, New Almaden, California; North Texas State Historical Collections, Denton, Texas; Adirondack Museum, Blue Mountain Lake, N. Y.

B. Lumbering and Gathering Naval Stores

1. *Bucks County Historical Society.*—Tools for felling, splitting, and log sawing (i.e., crosscut saws, pit saws, and a vertical sawmill), for moving and measuring including logging wheels and chains, for gathering turpentine, for holding and gripping logs, and for surfacing, chopping, and paring lumber.

2. *Henry Ford Museum, Dearborn, Mich.*—Several hundred tools for measuring standing lumber, felling trees, moving logs and timbers, barking, trimming and squaring, surfacing, and chopping, one circular sawmill, a water powered vertical gate sawmill, and an up-and-down sawmill.

3. *State Historical Society of Wisconsin.*—About 40 to 50 hand tools, mostly used in northern Wisconsin forests.

4. *Other institutions.*—Detroit Historical Museum, Detroit, Mich.; Logging Camp Museum, Hartwick Pines State Park, Grayling, Mich.;

Daniel Parrish Witter Agricultural Museum, Syracuse, N. Y.; Collier State Park Logging Museum, Klamath Falls, Ore.; Wethersfield Historical Society, Wethersfield, Conn.; Colonial Williamsburg, Williamsburg Va.;* Old Sturbridge Village, Sturbridge, Mass.; New York State Historical Association, Cooperstown, N. Y.

C. Farming

1. *Henry Ford Musem.**—Groups of artifacts depict the development of agricultural equipment from hand tools to machinery, with the emphasis upon processing grains. Objects of particular interest: plows, including John Deere's steel plow of 1840, harrows, mowers, rakes, hand reaping implements, threshers and reapers (thresher, 1841; McClure thresher, 1843, and reaper, ca. 1848), and fanning mills.

2. *Bucks County Historical Society.*—An extensive assortment of hand and animal driven implements for haying and threshing (a large collection of winnowing devices, scythes, flails, cradles, stationary thresher, ca. 1830–1840, clover headers, and fanning mills), plows, harrows, wood rakes, seed drills, cultivators, potato sorters, digging equipment, a land roller, and maple sugaring equipment.

3. *New York State Historical Association.**—A collection of implements and devices of the 1790–1860 period largely from New York State highlighted by an operating farm. Some of the more unusual objects are a hops press and other processing equipment, and an eighteenth-century German-type plow.

4. *Smithsonian Institution.*—Collection emphasizes hand tools and implements and early mechanical devices in full scale, replica, and patent model size in such areas as cultivation, swing, and moldboard plows, rakes, reapers and mowers, and corn and cotton seed planters. Of particular interest are the group of plows (New England, 1740; Pennsylvania, 1807; wheeled plow, 1769, Charles McCormick cast iron plow, and Nourie Eagle plow); a large group of reapers and mowers and models of these including 1831, 1834, 1843, 1847 McCormick reapers, Hussey reapers, 1833 and 1850, and a Belle reaper, 1828; and several hundred patent models.

5. *Pennsylvania Farm Museum of Landis Valley, Lancaster, Pa.*— Several thousand hand implements and machinery illustrating many phases of agricultural activity, especially early plows, harrows, cultivation and harvesting tools.

6. *Daniel Parrish Witter Agricultural Museum.*—Varied collection of plows, hay hoisting forks, and hops processing equipment.

* Denotes demonstrations by museum personnel.

7. *Other museums.*—Jamestown Visitor Center, Colonial National Historical Park, Jamestown, Va. (17th-century tools excavated at Jamestown); Nassau County Historical Museum, East Meadow, N. Y. (mostly of Long Island origin); Julia Meek Gaar Wayne County Historical Museum, Richmond, Ind. (Indiana pioneer farm equipment); Ohio Historical Society, Columbus, Ohio (a restored 1840 greenhouse); Los Angeles County Museum of History and Science, Los Angeles, Calif.; Society for the Preservation of New England Antiquities, Boston, Mass. (18th- and 19th-century wood farm implements); Old Sturbridge Village* (an operating New England farm of the 1760–1840 era); Shelburne Museum, Shelburne, Vt. (Vermont and New Hampshire farm equipment); Durell Farm Museum, Columbus, Ohio; Old Museum Village of Smith's Clove, Monroe, New York; Harold Warp Pioneer Village, Minden, Neb.; Old Salem, Winston-Salem, N. C.*

D. Ice Harvesting

Tools such as ice saws, spades, tongs, and other cutting devices.

1. *Henry Ford Museum*
2. *Skenesborough Museum, Whitehill, N. Y.*
3. *Adirondack Center Museum, Elizabethtown, N. Y.*
4. *Adirondack Museum, Blue Mountain Lake, N. Y.*
5. *Bucks County Historical Society*
6. *New York State Historical Association*

E. Whaling

1. *Smithsonian Institution.*—Equipment used for killing whales as well as tools for converting whale to usable products, i.e., harpoons, guns, ladles, and fleshers.

2. *Peabody Museum, Salem, Mass.*—A variety of toggle iron harpoons, lances, flue irons, temple irons, a blubber culling spade, a porpoise grainer, and blubber pikes and forks.

3. *Nantucket Historical Association, Nantucket, Mass.*—A comprehensive holding of whaling artifacts including scrimshaw, whale boats, lances, harpoons, flensing irons, and spades.

4. *Other institutions.*—Mystic Seaport Marine Historical Association, Mystic, Conn. (whaling guns and bomb guns); Bucks County Historical Society (boats, harpoon guns, kettles, andirons); Old Dartmouth Historical Society Whaling Museum, New Bedford, Mass. (a wide variety of such artifacts as harpoons, spades, and lances and a large collection of models); Salem Maritime National Historic Site, Salem, Mass.; Mariners Museum, Newport News, Va.; Suffolk County Whaling Museum of Sag Harbor, Long Island, N. Y.; Henry Ford Museum.

III. MANUFACTURING

A. *Process-related Artifacts*

1. *Metals.—*

   a) Hopewell Village, Elverson, Pa.—A restored 1840 iron-making village with a blast furnace,* anthracite furnace, charcoal hearth,* and water-powered blast machinery including tuyère arch.

   b) Cornwall Furnace, Cornwall, Pa.*—A restored 1856 iron blast furnace and foundry with a water-powered bellows, sulphur roasting ovens, and other furnace equipment.

   c) Saugus Ironworks Restoration, Saugus, Mass.—Restored 17th-century iron works, including such artifacts as the furnace waterwheel and tools used at the furnace.

   d) Other institutions.—Ohio Historical Society (300-acre charcoal iron furnace site, in the process of being restored); Maramec Iron Works, St. James, Mo.; Early Iron Village of Batsto, Egg Harbor City, N. J.; Adirondack Center Museum, Elizabethtown, N. Y. (site of water-powered blast furnace); New Almaden Museum (ore crushers).

2. *Textiles.—*

   a) Smithsonian Institution.—Collection traces the processing of fibers from raw material to cloth to finished product through artifacts, full-size models of machines, and patent models, i.e., Eli Whitney cotton gin; a sizable collection of spindles, looms, and power looms, including Jacquard loom, 1840; Slater water frame, 1790; Merrimack spinning frame, 1822; a Scholfield carding machine, 1803; and a very extensive collection of sewing and needle work implements highlighted by several hundred pre-Civil War sewing machines and relevant patent models.

   b) Merrimack Valley Textile Museum, North Andover, Mass.*—Collection illustrates the various processes of woolen cloth manufacture through such objects as early 19th-century wool picking machine, a carding machine, ca. 1810–1830, Amos Miner accelerated spinning heads, mid-19th-century spinning jack, full scale replica of Christopher Tully's 1775 spinning jenny, and 19th-century power looms.

   c) Old Sturbridge Village.—Highlight of collection is a water-powered carding mill having two pickers and three carding machines, two of which date from the 1800–1820 era.

   d) Old Slater Mill Museum, Pawtucket, R. I.—Artifacts are those used by textile companies during the lifetime of Samuel Slater (1768–1835). Besides four machines made in Lowell, Mass., in 1822, there are replicas of Slater's carding machine, 1790; Crompton's mule of 1779, and two Arkwright machines; and an original Arkwright carding machine, all housed in the restored Slater Mill of 1793.

e) Other institutions.—Henry Ford Museum* (Jacquard loom, carding machine and fly shuttle loom); Bucks County Historical Society; Do All Museum, Des Plaines, Ill.; New Jersey Historical Society, Newark, N. J.; Old Economy, Ambridge, Pa.; New York State Historical Association* (flax processing); Colonial Williamsburg.*

3. *Glass.*—

a) Corning Museum of Glass, Corning, N. Y.*—Furnaces, pucellas, pontils, glass pot, molds, and related equipment for making Steuben glass.

b) Jamestown Visitor Center, Colonial National Historical Park.*—A reconstructed 17th-century glass furnace with associated tools.

c) Other institutions.—Old Sturbridge Village.

4. *Tanning.*—Tanning artifacts other than hand tools have almost disappeared. The only known surviving pre-Civil War American tanyards are owned by private individuals, i.e., the Eisenhaure Family Farm, North Reading, Mass. The collections of the Bucks County Historical Society, however, do contain a bark mill and a beaming bench.

5. *Gunpowder and Chemicals.*—

a) Hagley Museum, Wilmington, Del.—Buildings of 19th-century black powder manufactory in various stages of construction, with such machinery as gearing and ten-ton cast iron mill wheels; the museum also has pilot models of rolling wheels and scale models of such milling techniques as rolling, stamping, and glazing.

6. *Food Preparation.*—

a) Smithsonian Institution.—A cider mill and two water-powered grist mills including gearing.

b) Henry Ford Museum.—Mill stones, wheels, and other equipment from 1832 Michigan grist mill,* and two cider mills.

c) Nassau County Historical Museum.—A tidal flour mill restored to the operative conditions of the early 1800's.

d) Delaware State Museum, Dover, Del.—A grist mill and early copper still used for making peach brandy.

e) Los Angeles County Museum.—An olive mill and copper stills.

f) Minnesota Historical Society Museum, St. Paul, Minnesota.— A reconstructed grist mill, 1856; wood gearing and spouts from the Pillsbury Mills.

g) Other institutions.—Colonial Williamsburg* (an 18th-century reconstructed wind-powered grist mill); Barton Museum of Whisky History, Bardstown, Ky.; Ohio Historical Society (turbine driven mill); Society for Preservation of New England Antiquities; Old Sturbridge Village* (an operating grist mill); Falstaff Museum of Brewing, St. Louis, Mo. (12 brewing kettles and a corking machine, 1850); Old Salem;* Bucks County Historical Society (complete 18th-century still).

7. *Other processes.*—Ropemaking (Mystic Seaport,* an operating 19th-century ropewalk; Old Sturbridge Village, ropemaking machine; New York State Historical Association,* ropemaking); paintmaking (Old Sturbridge Village and Delaware State Museum, paint pigment grinders); soapmaking (Colonial Williamsburg,* New York State Historical Association,* Old Sturbridge Village,* and Shelburne*); broommaking (New York State Historical Association* and Old Sturbridge Village,* broommaking machines).

B. *Product-related Artifacts*

Most public museums, company museums, and historical societies in the United States have artifacts which could be listed in this section especially in the case of objects that fit into the "decorative arts" category. Such institutions as the Henry Francis du Pont Winterthur Museum, Winterthur, Del., the Henry Ford Museum, Cleveland Museum of Art, Newark Museum, the Brooklyn Museum, the Dallas Museum of Fine Arts, the Metropolitan Museum of Art in New York, and the Boston Museum of Fine Arts have extensive holdings in most of these areas. Other museums have more specialized collections of relevant finished products, i.e., the Merrimack Valley Textile Museum, the Cooper Union Museum, New York, N. Y., and the Textile Museum, Washington, D.C., textile fabrics; the Bucks County Historical Society and the Bostonian Society, Boston, Mass., fire backs and stove plates; the Bennington Museum, Bennington, Vt., pottery; the Haverhill Historical Society, Haverhill, Mass., shoes; the Dard Hunter Paper Museum, Appleton, Wis., paper products; and the Chase Manhattan Bank Money Museum, New York, and Money Museum of the National Bank of Detroit, currency. Because of the almost endless number of objects, only a random selection is noted above, and the listing below does not include the numerous collections that fall within this category, except for firearms and heating and lighting devices.

1. *Firearms.*—

    a) Milwaukee Public Museum, Milwaukee, Wis.—An extremely large and varied collection of firearms and other weapons from the colonial era to modern times.

    b) Old Sturbridge Village.—Collection of American-made guns (133 pistols and 105 shoulder guns); of particular interest are the colonial arms, the U.S. models of official muskets and rifles from 1795 onward, group of New England pistols, the Kentucky flintlocks, and the Harrington Collection of gun models.

    c) Smithsonian Institution.—A fairly good selection of basic ignition systems including Colts, Remingtons, Whitneys, and Sharps, a large holding of patent models, and an extensive group of cartridges illustrating the development of the cartridge from paper to center firing.

    d) Springfield Armory, Benton Small Arms Museum, Springfield, Mass.—10,000 items showing evolution of military firearms.

    e) Winchester Gun Museum, New Haven, Conn.—5,000 American and European-made guns, some of which predate the Civil War.

    f) Other institutions.—Henry Ford Museum; the Bostonian Society; Essex Institute, Salem, Mass.; Mystic Seaport; Do All Museum; Cornwall Furnace; Jamestown Visitor Center, Colonial National Historical Park; Colonial Williamsburg; Buffalo and Erie County Historical Society, Buffalo, N. Y.; Mariners Museum; Browning Armory, Morgan, Utah; Detroit Historical Museum; Los Angeles County Museum; Bucks County Historical Society; Franklin Institute; Philadelphia, Pa. (Simeon North Collection); J. Woodman Higgins Armory, Worcester, Mass.; Metropolitan Museum of Art, N. Y.; Pennsylvania Farm Museum of Landis Valley; Colonial Williamsburg (Magazine representing a working 18th-century armory); Fort Ticonderoga, Ticonderoga, N. Y.

2. *Heating.*—

    a) Bucks County Historical Society.—Collection consists of an original Franklin stove, a large assortment of six- and ten-plate stoves and draft stoves, and a unique group of iron plates from a number of pre-Civil War American furnaces.

b) Henry Ford Museum.—A representative collection of heating devices centered on Franklin-type stoves including an "Elizabeth furnace," wood and coal grates, and assorted footwarmers.

c) Other institutions.—Smithsonian Institution; Pennsylvania Farm Museum of Landis Valley; New York State Historical Association; Old Sturbridge Village; Shelburne Museum; Colonial Williamsburg; Old Museum Village of Smith's Clove.

3. *Lighting.*—

a) Henry Ford Museum.—An extremely large and varied collection of lighting devices illustrating the development of lighting techniques from the ancient eras to contemporary America.

b) Smithsonian Institution.—A truly significant group, both as to size and variety, of lighting devices including open lamps, lamps of the inventive period, lanterns, and candle sticks as well as patent models.

c) Old Museum Village of Smith's Clove.—500 lamps and lanterns illustrating history of lighting in America from the rush light to the incandescent lamp.

d) Other institutions.—Henry Francis du Pont Winterthur Museum; Essex Institute; Colonial Williamsburg; Old Sturbridge Village.

IV. TOOLS AND INSTRUMENTS

A. *Tools of the Craftsmen*

1. *Metalwork.*—

a) Colonial Williamsburg.—Blacksmith equipment* including three forges (one traveling), bellows, swage blocks, vises, hack saws, calipers, screwplate; gunsmith,* the engraving tools, rifling and boring machine, boring rig, cutting dies, reamers, and bullet moulds; pewterer,* original 18th-century button and spoon moulds; silversmith,* wire drawing machines, bellows, engraving tools, hammers, anvils, and moulds.

b) Bucks County Historical Society.—Filemaker, complete set of tools; tinsmith tools including wire drawing; a large group of blacksmith tools; pewterers' tools, moulds and tools for casting iron; engraving tools for copper and steel; gunsmiths' tools and bullet moulds.

c) Old Sturbridge Village.—Blacksmith,* bellows, anvils, froes, tongs, dividers, forging hammer, tire settingstone; pewter, spoon, and button moulds; tinsmith, an extensive collection of tools; gunsmith, reaming machine, rifling machine, bullet moulds, and assorted hand tools; and such miscellaneous equipment as wire drawing machine and dies, rolling machines.

d) Henry Ford Museum.—The tools for such craftsmen as the gunsmith, locksmith, pewterer,* tinsmith,* blacksmith,* and silversmith.

e) Other institutions.—Mystic Seaport (shipsmith tools,* i.e., bellows, hammers, anvils, swedges); New York State Historical Association* (blacksmith and tinsmith); Smithsonian Institution (scattered tools and engraving equipment); Hopewell Village (blacksmith shop); Franklin Institute (coining press used in the U.S. Mint); Jamestown Visitor Center, Colonial National Historical Park (excavated 17th-century tools); Ohio Historical Society (blacksmith and tinsmith tools); Detroit Historical Museum (blacksmith and gunsmith); Old Salem (gunsmith,* tinsmith,* and silversmith); Nantucket Historical Association (shipsmiths tools); Cornwall Furnace (iron makers tools); Shelburne Museum* (blacksmith and patterns for brass and bronze casting); Old Museum Village of Smith's Clove (blacksmith); Essex Institute (silversmith); Durell Farm Museum; Henry Francis du Pont Winterthur Museum* (Dominy Workshop).

2. Woodwork.—

a) Shelburne Museum.—An extensive collection of tools for a variety of craftsmen, i.e., chairmaker, cooper, coachmaker, wheelwright, cabinetmaker, shinglemaker, and bowlmaker; such equipment as adzes, axes, all types of planes, chisels, gauges, routers, scrapers, saws and hammers, and shinglemaking machines are represented; of particular interest are the tools used to make other woodworking tools.

b) Smithsonian Institution.—A variety of drills, planes, chisels, lathes, and boring and shaving machines.

c) The Henry Francis du Pont Winterthur Museum.—The Dominy Workshop* Collection of 18th- and 19th-century tools (1000 items) for the cabinetmaker, house and mill carpenter, wheelwright, and cooper; including such small objects as hammers, chisels, drills, planes, calipers, saws, and templates or patterns for woodworking; and such larger pieces as original benches, one pole lathe, and a great wheel lathe.

d) Henry Ford Museum.—A representative collection containing several thousand tools, including levels, squares, dividers, pit saws, veneer saws, planes, jointers, shavers, draw knives, rasps, vises, augers, reamers, braces, and calipers; a few specialized shipwright and cabinetmaker tools; and equipment for making wood pumps.

e) Colonial Williamsburg.*—18th-century tools for the cabinetmaker, cooper, shinglemaker, carpenter, and the wheelwright.

f) Old Sturbridge Village.*—The Wing Collection of 18th-century cabinetmakers' equipment, and tools for the cooper, wheelwright, pipemaker; of particular interest are a foot-powered jig saw, a 17th-century treadle wood lathe, and a mortice borer.

g) Bucks County Historical Society.—Several hundred tools for the cabinetmaker, cooper, wheelwright, pump and wood pipemakers, chairmakers (including forms and patterns), shinglemakers, and fencemakers.

h) New York State Historical Association.—Tools illustrating shinglemaking, coopering, woodworking, wood pumpmaking.

i) Other institutions.—Mystic Seaport (cooper, wood carver and shipbuilder tools); Old Salem* (joiner and cooper); Roberson Memorial Center, Binghamton, N. Y. (building); New Jersey Historical Society (general woodworking); Los Angeles County Museum; Delaware State Museum (shinglemaker and pumpmaker); Peabody Museum (ship carpenter, joiner, cooper); Julia Meek Gaar Wayne County Historical Museum (collection of planes); Old Economy (cabinetmaker and cooper); Nassau County Historical Museum (cabinetmaker and house builder); State Historical Society of Missouri, Columbia, Mo.; Skenesborough Museum (carpenter, cooper, cabinetmaker and shipbuilder); the Toolhouse, East Aurora, N. Y. (shipbuilder); Jamestown Visitor Center, Colonial National Historical Park (17th-century remains of woodworkers' tools); Buffalo and Erie County Historical Society (cabinetmaker, cooper, and carpenter); Canal Museum (boatbuilder); Daniel Parrish Witter Agricultural Museum (car-

penter and cooper); Cabrillo Beach Marine Museum, San
Pedro, Calif. (shipbuilding tools); Mariners Museum (shipbuilding tools); Pennsylvania Farm Museum of Landis Valley
(carpenter, cabinetmaker, and cooper); Historical Society of
Delaware, Wilmington, Del. (cabinetmaker and carpenter);
Maryland Historical Society, Baltimore, Md. (shipbuilding
tools); Durell Farm Museum.

3. *Pottery Making.*—
   a) Bucks County Historical Society.—Contents of a 19th-century
      Pennsylvania pottery, including moulds, forms, tile wheel,
      potter's wheel, querns, paint and glaze kiln, and sand tubs.
   b) Smithsonian Institution.—Hand tools, moulds, patterns, and
      kiln furniture used at the Thompson Pottery in West Vir-
      ginia from the late 18th century throughout the 19th century.
   c) Other institutions.—Old Salem; Litchfield Historical Society,
      Litchfield, Conn. (potter's wheel); Old Sturbridge Village*
      (a reconstructed kiln, glaze mill, ribs for shaping, and a pug
      mill); Henry Ford Museum;* Bennington Museum, Ben-
      nington, Vermont; Jamestown Visitor Center, Colonial Na-
      tional Historical Park (17th-century tool fragments); New
      York State Historical Association (tools).

4. *Glassmaking.*—
   a) Corning Museum of Glass.—An extensive collection of glass
      blowing and etching equipment.
   b) Old Sturbridge Village (moulds, glass pots, pucellas, jacks,
      blocks, pontils, blow pipes, trimming shears, and bench).
   c) Other institutions.—Henry Ford Museum (pontils and blow-
      pipes); Smithsonian Institution (12 representative tools);
      Bucks County Historical Society; New Jersey Historical Soci-
      ety (crucibles); Bennington Museum (pressed glass pat-
      terns); Ohio Historical Society (glass blowing tools); James-
      town Visitor Center, Colonial National Historical Park*
      (glass blowing tools).

5. *Leatherwork.*—
   a) Colonial Williamsburg.*—An extensive collection of such
      shoemaker and cobblers' tools as hammers, lasts, stirrups,
      awls, crimpers, and pincers and harnessmaking equipment.
   b) Shelburne Museum.—Tools used by the currier, shoemaker,
      and harnessmaker; one of the few collections containing
      tools associated with tanning.

c) Delaware State Museum.—An extensive collection of harness-maker's tools and equipment; also, a smaller but representative collection of shoemaker's tools.

d) Other institutions.—Hagley Museum (tanning and currying tools); Smithsonian Institution (shoemaker's tools); Suffolk Museum and Carriage House, Stony Brook, N. Y. (harness and saddle maker's tools); Bucks County Historical Society (several hundred harnessmaker's and shoemaker's equipment); New York State Historical Association (shoemaking and a few pieces of currying tools); Julia Meek Gaar Wayne County Historical Museum (shoemakers); Old Economy (shoemakers); Old Salem (shoemakers); Sandwich Historical Society Museum, Center Sandwich, N. H. (shoemakers); Bennington Museum (shoemakers and harnessmakers); Haverhill Historical Society (shoemakers); Essex Institute (cobblers); Henry Ford Museum (shoemakers and harnessmakers).

6. *Spinning, Weaving, Dyeing, and Sewing.—*
   a) Smithsonian Institution.—A sizable collection of spindles, looms, 4- and 6-arm clock reels, spinning wheels, spin ginners and an extensive collection of sewing and needle work implements highlighted by several hundred pre-Civil War sewing machines and relevant patent models.

   b) Merrimack Valley Textile Museum.—Collection of reels, niddy-noddies, warping frames, hand looms, tape looms, bobbins, shuttles, weaver's tools, and teasels.

   c) Nassau County Historical Society.—Approximately 200 pieces of spinning and weaving equipment for household processing of flax and wool.

   d) Other institutions.—Old Sturbridge Village;* Colonial Williamsburg;* New York State Historical Association;* Bucks County Historical Society; Old Slater Mill Museum; Old Salem (dyeing and weaving equipment); Daniel Parrish Witter Agricultural Museum (flax and wool processing equipment); State Historical Society of Wisconsin (spinning equipment used in the home); Julia Meek Gaar Wayne County Historical Museum (spinning wheels and looms for flax and wool); Henry Ford Museum* (equipment for flax, silk, wool, and cotton processing); Nantucket Historical Association (sailmaker's tools); Mystic Seaport (weaving and sailmaking); Maryland Historical Society (rigger and sail-maker's tools).

7. *Papermaking.—*

   a) Dard Hunter Paper Museum, Appleton, Wis.—Papermaking moulds dating from 1784 and models of first papermaking machinery.

   b) Crane Museum, Dalton, Mass.—Model of a one vat paper mill (ca. 1801–1840) and moulds.

   c) Other institutions.—Smithsonian Institution (papermaking moulds); Bucks County Historical Society (papermaking moulds); Colonial Williamsburg* (papermaking moulds); Franklin Institute (operating model of early 19th-century papermaking machine).

B. *Culinary Tools*

1. *Henry Ford Museum.*—A wide variety of such wood or metal utensils as parers, peelers, pitters, squeezers, coffee and meat grinders, spice mills, chopping knives, sausage stuffers, rolling pins, and dairying equipment, including churns and cheese presses.

2. *Bucks County Historical Society.*—Collection includes equipment for dairying (churns, butter prints and moulds, ladles and lard stuffers), meat processing (grinders, cleavers, knives, hooks, sausage stuffers), fruit processing (peelers and crusher), confectioner's tools, grinders for corn and rice, and solar salt processing equipment.

3. *Smithsonian Institution.*—Holdings include both hand and mechanical devices for home and commercial use; the dairy collection including Gayle Borden's vacuum can and milk condensing equipment is especially large and varied; other categories are butchering and meat processing equipment; collection is weak in canning apparatus.

4. *Other institutions.*—Old Sturbridge Village* (several hundred items of 1790–1840 period including baking); New York State Historical Association* (items date from 1780–1860 including baking and cheese-making); Colonial Williamsburg* (17th- and 18th-century hand utensils including baking); Old Salem; Old Museum Village of Smith's Clove; Shelburne Museum; Old Economy (1825–1830 kitchen for feeding 1,000 people, early canning equipment, and wine cellar apparatus); Julia Meek Gaar Wayne County Historical Museum; State Historical Society of Wisconsin; Daniel Parrish Witter Agricultural Museum; Jamestown Visitor Center, Colonial National Historical Park (17th-century excavated artifacts, including brew house items); Hopewell Village* (baking).

C. Machine Tools

1. *Henry Ford Museum.*—An especially significant group having lathes (New Hampshire, ca. 1845; chain feed and weighted carriage, 1850 period; chain feed, 1845 period; strop lathe; foot-powered wood turning lathes, and Maudslay lathe, 1828); a punch press, St. Louis, ca. 1840; a wood circular planer, 1853; a shingle cutter; two early nail machines; slotters; and a gear cutter, 1850 type.

2. *Smithsonian Institution.*—Collection contains several full-size machines, many models of machines, and a few patent models, i.e., iron planer, mid-1840's; Robertson milling machine, 1852; Lincoln milling machine, lathes (metal cutting lathe, 1830, Rhode Island engine lathe, 1830–1840; Robins and Laurence lathe, 1853); linear and circular dividing engine, 1859; and screw cutting tool, 1766.

3. *Do All Museum.*—Full-size replicas of John Wilkinson's boring mill and Henry Maudslay's screw cutting lathe, and scale models of Eli Whitney's milling machine, Richard Roberts' metal planer, and James Nasmyth's drill press.

4. *Old Sturbridge Village.*—Reaming machines, borers, wood turning lathes, and gear cutting machine with base (Trenton, N. J., 1836).

5. *Other institutions.*—Springfield Armory (Blanchard lathe, 1822, and gun stocking machine); Daniel Parrish Witter Agricultural Museum (foot-powered lathe).

D. Clocks and Watches

1. *California Academy of Sciences, San Francisco, Calif.*—Doctor W. Barclay Stephens Horological Collection of several thousand items from all eras and parts of the world.

2. *Smithsonian Institution.*—A large, varied collection containing all types of instruments from many sections of the United States, and tools for making the objects. Of particular interest are the tools and products of the early 19th-century Bond of Boston Shop; a Connecticut tower clock movement, 1830; first chronograph made in the United States; a variety of early pocket watches; and a Rittenhouse regulator clock, ca. 1769.

3. *Old Sturbridge Village.*—Primarily New England wall, shelf, and grandfather clocks of the 18th and 19th centuries, especially of the Willard family; also, some tools such as gear cutting engines.

4. *Hagans Clock Manor Museum, Evergreen, Colo.*—Over 6,000 European and American time keeping devices.

5. *Other institutions.*—Bucks County Historical Society (dies and

cutting tools); American Clock and Watch Museum, Bristol, Conn.;
Mystic Seaport (New England clocks); Henry Francis du Pont Winterthur Museum (Dominy Clock Shop and Forge); Connecticut Historical
Society, Hartford, Conn. (Daniel Burnap's tools); Colonial Williamsburg; Metropolitan Museum of Art; Henry Ford Museum (clocks).

E. Navigational Instruments

1. *Smithsonian Institution.*—Several collections such as the Ellicott
and the Pike Collections and other miscellaneous holdings contain
quadrants, mercurial barometers, telescopes, astrolabes, and compasses.

2. *Peabody Museum.*—A very extensive collection including quadrants, astrolabes, sextants, compasses, nocturnals, ring dial, chronom-
eter, and log-timers.

3. *Mystic Seaport.*—Holdings consist of a wide variety of instruments,
including cross staffs, log glass, wood compasses, octants, chronometers,
quadrants (especially Davis quadrants), and sextants.

4. *Mariners Museum.*—Quadrants, sextants, octants, astrolabes, compasses, and chronometers form the nucleus of the holdings.

5. *Other institutions.*—Bucks County Historical Society; Nantucket
Historical Association (sextants and quadrants); Penobscot Marine
Museum, Searsport, Me.; Delaware State Museum (wind gauges, sex-
tants, quadrants, compasses); New-York Historical Society, New York,
N. Y.; Museum of the City of New York; Buffalo and Erie County
Historical Society; Marine Museum of the Seaman's Church Institute,
New York, N. Y. (sextants, octants, compasses, and planespheres); Cali-
fornia Academy of Sciences; Cranbrook Institute of Science, Bloomfield
Hills, Mich.; Franklin Institute; Henry Ford Museum (sextants and
related equipment).

F. Surveying Instruments

1. *Smithsonian Institution.*—Includes equal altitude instruments,
compasses and staff heads, tally pins and marker, chains, theodolites,
transit compasses, solar compasses, inclinometer, and a demi-circle.

2. *Minnesota Historical Society Museum.*—A collection of equipment used to survey the Minnesota territory in the mid-1800's.

3. *Gurley Museum of Surveying Instruments, Troy, N. Y.*—Nineteen
American instruments predating 1858, including compasses, levels,
transits, a circumferentor, and theodolites.

4. *Other institutions.*—Old Salem; Mystic Seaport (nautical surveying); Peabody Museum (nautical surveying); Bucks County Historical
Society; Henry Ford Museum (including David Rittenhouse arti-

facts); Ohio Historical Society; Sandwich Historical Society; State Historical Society of Wisconsin; Canal Museum; Mariners Museum (nautical surveying); Buffalo and Erie County Historical Society; White Memorial Foundation, Litchfield, Conn. (compasses); Cabrillo Beach Marine Museum; Do All Museum; Cranbrook Institute; Old Sturbridge Village (wood and metal compasses); Franklin Institute (levels, graphometers, and compasses including ones made by David Rittenhouse, Thomas Greenough, William Young, and Stancliffe Draper).

G. Medical and Pharmaceutical Instruments

1. *Smithsonian Institution.*—Collections are particularly strong in pharmacy and dentistry; also a limited number of American simple and compound microscopes, magnifying glasses, O. V. Black Collection of Surgical Instruments, and patent models of an articulator and a vaccinator.

2. *Medical Museum of the Armed Forces Institute of Pathology, Washington, D.C.*—A bloodletting kit and two lancets, a wide variety of dental instruments (1838–1850), stethoscopes (1816–1850), microscopes, and surgical instruments.

3. *Stabler-Leadbeater Apothecary Museum, Alexandria, Va.*—Furnishings and equipment for a Virginia apothecary shop of the 1790–1860 era, including bottles, scales, mortars, and pestles.

4. *Dr. Samuel Shaw House, Plainfield, Mass.*—An early 19th-century physician's office and equipment containing an extensive collection of instruments, dispensary equipment, and office furniture.

5. *Other institutions.*—New York State Historical Association (doctor's office and drug store, both ca. 1840 in origin, and veterinarian equipment); Julia Meek Gaar Wayne County Historical Museum (apothecary shop and a few medical instruments); Mütter Museum of the College of Physicians, Philadelphia, Pa. (bleeding instruments, stethoscopes, microscopes, mortars, pestles, physicians' cases, and dental equipment); Museum of Medical Progress, Prairie du Chien, Wis. (surgical kits, bleeding kits, and wood stethoscopes); Jamestown Visitor Center, Colonial National Historical Park; Buffalo and Erie County Historical Society (surgical, dental, and apothecary); Peabody Museum (ship medical equipment); North Texas State Historical Collections (surgical kit, bleeders, lancets, drug mill, mortars, and pestles); Historical Museum of Wabash Valley, Terre Haute, Ind. (obstetrician's equipment); State of Alabama Department of Archives and History, Montgomery, Ala.; Lederle Institutional Museum, Pearl River, N. Y. (microscopes, medicine kits, and veterinarian kits); Bostonian Society

(surgeons' tools); and the following apothecary shops: Old Sturbridge Village (apothecary and physician); State Historical Society of Wisconsin (pharmaceutical apparatus and equipment); La Pharmacie Francaise, New Orleans, La.; Spring Mill Village Apothecary Shop, Mitchell, Ind.; Hugh Mercer Apothecary Shop in Fredericksburg, Va.; Pasteur Galt Shop in Williamsburg, Va.; and Southern California Pharmaceutical Association, Los Angeles, Calif. (mid-19th-century drug store); Shelburne Museum; Henry Ford Museum.

H. *Other Scientific Equipment and Apparatus*

1. *Smithsonian Institution.*—Extensive holdings in a wide variety of categories, including chemistry, physics, meteorology, astronomy, weights and measures, and mathematics. Of particular interest are the Williams College chemical furnace, 18th century; the Joseph Priestley group of laboratory equipment; Hare's apparatus for thermal conductivity; harmonic motion apparatus; bell jars; Atwood machine, 1829; patent models of various Fairbanks scales; gas meters, 1842, 1850, 1854; barometers, both mercurial and aneroid; thermometers, sea sounding apparatus, 1837; calculating rules; drawing instruments, orreries, an astronomical telescope, terrestrial telescopes, diffraction grates and mirrors, and rain gauges.

2. *Lederle Institutional Museum.*—A variety of chemical and refining apparatus.

3. *Other institutions.*—New Jersey Historical Society (2 drawing instruments); Do All Museum (chemical box); Jamestown Visitor Center, Colonial National Historical Park (17th-century excavated artifacts); Hopewell Village (wagon scales); Bartlett Memorial Historical Museum, Beloit, Wisc. (set of chemical laboratory equipment); Cranbrook Institute (draftsmen's instruments, weights and measures, celestial and terrestrial spheres, and telescopes); Merrimack Valley Textile Museum (water flow testing devices); Henry Ford Museum (chemical scales, barometers); Franklin Institute (boiler material testing machine, 1831; Priestley's air pump and tongs; fresnel lenses; and telescopes); Old Sturbridge Village (wood and metal compasses, odometers, draftsmen's instruments, barometer, microscopes, telescopes).

V. POWER

A. *Animal*

1. *Old Sturbridge Village.*—Horse and dog treadmills, animal sweep-powered cider press, and a horse-powered pug mill.

2. *Old Museum Village of Smith's Clove.*—Dog, sheep, mule, and donkey treadmills.

3. *Bucks County Historical Society.*—Horse and dog tread mills; animal-powered equipment for pumping water; and animal-powered bark mill.

4. *Other institutions.*—New York State Historical Association (horse and dog tread mills and sweep power devices); Canal Museum (mule and horse-powered equipment for moving canal boats); Daniel Parrish Witter Agricultural Museum (one- and two-horse treadmills and varying sizes of dog treadmills); Collier State Park Logging Museum (horse-power crosscut saw); Franklin Institute (dog treadmill); Pennsylvania Farm Museum of Landis Valley (treadmills); Henry Ford Museum (treadmills and sweeps).

B. *Wind*

Several museum and historical societies have various types of windmills, some of which are in operating condition, i.e., Henry Ford Museum,* Colonial Williamsburg,* Daniel Parrish Witter Agricultural Museum, Nantucket Historical Association, and Los Angeles County Museum.

C. *Water*

Jefferson County Historical Society Museum, Watertown, N. Y. (thirty water turbines, some predating the Civil War); Old Sturbridge Village (an operating breast water wheel, and equipment from a rose wheel drive up and down sawmill); Hopewell Village (an operating pitchback water wheel); Nassau County Historical Museum (tidal grist mill); Ohio Historical Society (a turbine driven flour mill); Bucks County Historical Society (plumping mill or a water powered mortar and pestle); Hagley Museum* (a reconstructed breast water wheel).

D. *Steam, Hot Air, and Gas*

1. *Smithsonian Institution.*—Holdings consist of patent models and full-size objects, including a portion of cylinder of the first steam engine erected on the American continent; steam engines, 1819, 1829, 1830, 1838, 1850; patent models of Baker and Baldwin steam engine, 1839; pressure recorders, ca. 1796 and ca. 1842; patent model of Diesel gas engine, Perry, 1846; gas engines, Perry, 1844, Barnetts, 1838, and Brown, 1823; hot air engines, especially A. Lyman, 1854; and steam pumps.

2. *Henry Ford Museum.*—Both full size models and antiques of major European developments in steam power and an extensive group

of post-Watt, American-made steam and hot air engines from 1800 to the Civil War; of special interest are stationary steam engine, South Carolina, 1830–1850; stationary steam engine, Massachusetts, ca. 1850; stationary steam engine, Albany, 1848; Corliss steam engine, 1855; steam engine, Stillman and Allen, 1842, and a large group of hot air engines including some made by Ericsson.

3. *Other institutions.*—Buffalo and Erie County Historical Society (working models of steam engines); The Mariners Museum (models and full size steam engines); Do All Museum (James Watt steam engine, 1799 and scale model of Newcomen atmospheric engine); the Newcomen Society, West Chester, Pa. (working models of such developments as first table engine, Newcomen mine pumping plant, grasshopper steam engine, and Oliver Evans high pressure mill engine); Old Museum Village of Smith's Clove (steam engines).

E. *Electricity*

1. *Smithsonian Institution.*—Artifacts trace early evolution of electric power through electric wheels, electro-static machines, motors, generators, and other associated apparatus; of special interest are: Priestley electro-static machine, ca. 1800; The Joseph Henry Collection of apparatus, especially Henry's rocking motor, 1831; Charles G. Page, motor, 1839, magneto, 1845, and generator; therapeutic needles; Davis paddle wheel motor, ca. 1848; and Avery electro-magneto engine, 1851.

2. *Franklin Institute.*—Joseph Priestley's electro-static machine, lightning rods, and leyden jars.

3. *Henry Ford Museum.*—Galvanometer and Davis and Kitty electro-magneto, 1854.

VI. TRANSPORTATION

A. *Water* (*Ocean*)

1. *Mystic Seaport.*—Center of collection of sailing vessels are the schooner *Australia* allegedly built in the early 1800's, and the whaleship *Charles W. Morgan* constructed by Jethro and Zachariah Hillman, Fairbanks, Mass., 1841, including seven whaleboats; also, a large collection of small fishing craft, half models, rig models, and sailor-made models.

2. *Smithsonian Institution.*—Collection based upon illustrating the evolution of the merchant marine of the United States and the United States Navy; two full-size ships and the half models of both navy and

merchant marine vessels are the highlights of the collection; other interesting items are the rigship models and models of propellers and naval
ordnance.

3. *Mariners Museum.*—Extensive model collection of sail and steam,
merchant and naval vessels.

4. *Other institutions.*—Nantucket Historical Association (whaleboats); Portsmouth Naval Shipyard Museum, Portsmouth, Va. (dry-
dock in use 1833); Maryland Historical Society (half model of Chesapeake Bay craft); Shelburne Museum (SS *Ticonderoga*); San Francisco
Maritime Museum, San Francisco, Calif.; Peabody Museum (ship
models and harbor dredge); Chesapeake Bay Maritime Museum, St.
Michaels, Md.; Plimouth Plantation, Plymouth, Mass. (replica of *May-
flower*); Festival Park, Jamestown, Va. (replicas of the *Susan Constant,
Godspeed,* and *Discovery*).

B. Water (Inland)

1. *Canal Museum.*—Buildings used for boat weighing and toll assess-
ment; canal boat bits, cleats and pulleys, bilge pumps, and hooks; and
models of various types of canal boats.

2. *Buffalo and Erie County Historical Society.*—Ship models of
Great Lakes vessels and Erie Canal barges.

3. *Other institutions.*—National Museum of Transport, St. Louis,
Mo.; Do All Museum (replica of *Clermont*); Skenesborough Museum
(models of canal locks and lake steam boats); Minnesota Historical
Society Museum (Indian dugout canoe and Indian birch bark canoe);
Ohio Historical Society (four canal locks and models of canal and Great
Lakes boats); New York State Historical Association (a dugout canoe).

C. Land Vehicles (Animal Powered)

1. *Henry Ford Museum.*—An extensive and varied group of animal-
drawn vehicles, including wagons, carriages, carts, sleighs, and fire engines, i.e., Red River Cart, 1803–1880; dog cart, mid-19th century; rockaway, 1840–1870; the caleche, pre-Revolutionary War; two- and four-
wheel chaises; top buggies; Campbell coach, ca. 1795; Conestoga wagon;
peddler's wagon; Concord Coach; and six fire engines.

2. *Suffolk Museum and Carriage House.*—A large collection which
includes vehicles used for both work and pleasure, i.e., Boston chaise,
1810; coach, early 19th century; rockaway, ca. 1855; Conestoga wagon,
ca. 1820; open stage, ca. 1850; country wagon, 18th century; canopy top
country wagon, ca. 1860; two-seat pleasure wagon, 1820; a sled; and
several 18th- and early 19th-century sleighs.

3. *Shelburne Museum.*—Sleighs, commercial and farm wagons, fire equipment, gun carriages, chaises, carts, and surreys are several of the types of vehicles in this extensive collection; of interest: chaise, late 18th-century; doctor's gig, ca. 1800; Concord Wagon, ca. 1840; 6 passenger rockaway, ca. 1850; Abbott pleasure wagon, early 19th-century; family wagon, early 19th century; curtain rockaway, early 19th century; and one horse chaise, ca. 1830.

4. *Smithsonian Institution.*—Collection includes a few 18th-century vehicles, several 19th-century vehicles, as well as stone road markers of the 1820's and cast iron markers of the 1830's; a few fire engines; bicycles and wood hubs; highlights are: coachee, ca. 1810; gig, ca. 1810; 2 wheel fayette, ca. 1790; 4 wheel fayette, ca. 1860; Concord Coach; Conestoga wagon; farm wagon; and French boneshaker, ca. 1820.

5. *New York State Historical Association.*—Vehicles associated with the farm form the nucleus of the collection, i.e., two Connecticut wagons; several gigs and chaises; dog carts; sleighs; a freight wagon; maple sugaring wagon; oxcart; sledge; snow roller; tin peddler's wagon; and Concord Coach.

6. *Other institutions.*—Old Sturbridge Village (farm vehicles, carriages, and fire fighting equipment); Colonial Williamsburg (18th century vehicles both antique and reproductions); Nassau County Historical Museum (Long Island carriages, work wagons, and sleighs); Daniel Parrish Witter Agricultural Museum (carriages, sleighs, farm wagons); Gannon Museum of Wagons, Mabton, Wash. (Conestoga wagon, paneled pleasure wagon, sleigh); Detroit Historical Museum (Conestoga wagon); Granger Homestead Society, Canandaigua, N. Y. (coaches, carriages, and sleighs); Minnesota Historical Society Museum (oxcart and dog sled); Bucks County Historical Society (a large collection of fire engines and several carriages, wagons, sleighs); Franklin Institute (fire engines); Home Insurance Company, New York, N. Y. (fire fighting equipment); National Museum of Transport; Insurance Company of North America, Philadelphia, Pa. (an extensive collection of fire fighting apparatus); Elliott Museum, Stuart, Fla. (objects relating to evolution of the wheel).

D. Land (Railroad)

1. *Smithsonian Institution.*—Several full-size pieces of equipment, a large group of assorted patent models, a collection of track segments, bells, lamps, and such parts of equipment as boiler wheels and cylinders; of special interest, *Pioneer*, 1851, full size; all iron driving wheel from *DeWitt Clinton*, 1831; railroad car, ca. 1836, full size; boiler and walk-

ing beam from *Stourbridge Lion*, 1829; Farmer's electric locomotive, ca. 1847; and Collier's electric locomotive.

2. *Baltimore and Ohio Transportation Museum, Baltimore, Md.*— Four full size locomotives, *Atlantic*, 1832; *John Hancock*, 1835; *Memnon*, 1848; and *William Mason*, 1856, form the basis of this extensive collection of railroad memorabilia.

3. *Franklin Institute.*—Cross sections of railroad track and the full size locomotive made for the Peoples Railway, ca. 1842, and the *Rocket*, 1838.

4. *Other institutions.*—Henry Ford Museum (operating replica of *DeWitt Clinton*, two pre-Civil War locomotives, and track sections); Museum of Science and Industry, Chicago, Ill.; National Museum of Transport.

VII. COMMUNICATION

A. *Printing and Bookbinding*

1. *Henry Ford Museum.*—A very large and varied collection of both hand- and machine-powered presses. Some pieces are operable, i.e., a group of presses from Richard Hoe (including Seth Adams Press, ca. 1853; Washington Press, 1845; Acorn Hand Press, 1822); a Clymer Columbia Press; a Ramage Press, ca. 1850; Abraham Stansburg Press, New York, ca. 1822; John I. Wells Press, 1819; Foster Hand Press, 1853; and a Rust Press, 1821.

2. *Franklin Institute.*—Type making moulds; type from Ephrata, 1775; machine for cutting paper, 1852; such bookbinding tools as pots, bone folders, pallets, gilder wheels, beveling knives, and paring tools; two Ramage presses, and a hand paper press.

3. *Colonial Williamsburg.**—Bookbinding tools, including clamps, stamps, trimmers, large screw press, and hammers; a plow press; Common Press; ca. 1750 original type; and other hand presses.

4. *Smithsonian Institution.*—Wood hand press, 1720, used by Benjamin Franklin in England in 1726 and commonly called the Franklin press; John I. Wells all iron press, 1819; Adam Ramage press, ca. 1821; George Clymer's Columbian press; David Bruce, type casting machine, 1838; moulds for casting type, 18th century; patent models, and the Fox Talbot collection of plates and prints illustrating the beginning of photo and mechanical printing.

5. *Other institutions.*—Bucks County Historical Society (presses); Julia Meek Gaar Wayne County Historical Museum (press and type

setting equipment); Old Economy (wood press, ca. 1830); Ohio Historical Society (bookbinding tools); New York State Historical Association * (an operating printing office); Mystic Seaport * (an operating printing office); Old Sturbridge Village * (presses).

B. Photography

1. *Smithsonian Institution.*—Collection contains patent models, photographic lenses, a few cameras, and a variety of dark room equipment, i.e., a daguerrotype camera, ca. 1850, solar camera (enlarger), ca. 1850.

2. *George Eastman House, Rochester, N. Y.*—The chief items of interest are a daguerrotype camera, 1839, and a reproduction of a Talbot camera.

3. *Other institutions.*—Franklin Institute (fantascope, 1834); U.S. Army Signal Corps Museum, Fort Monmouth, N. J. (a daguerrotype camera, ca. 1854); Henry Ford Museum* (a daguerrotype camera and an operable tintype camera).

C. Telegraph

1. *Smithsonian Institution.*—Holdings include registers, relays, keys, fire alarm systems, cables and wires, and patent models of these innovations. Attention is called to: Morse-Vail telegraph key and register, 1844; Morse Telegraph, 1849; Farmer Telegraph Register, 1856; House printing telegraph, 1846; pieces of cables, especially Cyrus Field memorabilia.

2. *Museum of the City of New York.*—Memorabilia related to the early development of the telegraph.

3. *Other institutions.*—Henry Ford Museum (several weight-driven telegraphs, 1845–1855); Western Union Telegraph Museum (telegraph and cable items); Bell Telephone Laboratories, New York, N. Y. (telegraph receiver made by Samuel Morse, 1843, and pieces of cable); U.S. Army Signal Corps Museum (Beardslee Magneto Telegraph); Franklin Institute (S. F. B. Morse telegraph recorders).

INDEX